NEDLEY

DEPRESSION & ANXIETY

RECOVERY PROGRAM™

WORKBOOK

NEIL NEDLEY, MD

NEDLEY PUBLISHING
info@drnedley.com
www.nedleyhealthsolutions.com

580.226.8007
530.422.7902
888.778.4445

ISBN 13: 978-1-938028-00-7

CAUTION: This book and video series does not establish a doctor–patient relationship with the reader. Persons who are ill or on medication who wish to significantly change their lifestyle should do so under the direction of a physician familiar with the effects of lifestyle change on health.

DISCLAIMER: Dr. Nedley does not endorse all the views, opinions, or philosophies that may be advanced by the authors referenced in this book.

*The nutritional data used in this workbook and DVD are derived from the USDA database for standard reference. The values in four graphs differ from those found in *Depression: the Way Out*, which used ESHA for its standard of reference. When in question as to which graph to use, defer to the graph in the workbook as the most current and accurate value. (pg. 48, 49, 55)

SPECIAL THANKS:
Contributors: Paula Reiter, Erica Nedley, Miriam Popovski
Editors: Trisha Heddlesten, Kerri Hitt, Cami Martin
References: Nathan Hyde
Layout and Design: Aleksandar Popovski

Printed in China.

TABLE OF CONTENTS

Welcome to the Nedley Depression and Anxiety Recovery Program™

Congratulations on purchasing the most comprehensive program available on the subject of depression and anxiety recovery. Learn the lessons set before you well because they are life to you.

Whether you or a loved one are struggling with depression, anxiety, or other mental health challenges, there is good news. Depression and anxiety should not be tolerated as a lifelong condition—and this is why the *Nedley Depression and Anxiety Recovery Program™* focuses on the underlying and contributing causes of depression and anxiety—so that a lasting cure can be found. In order to participate, you need to have a willingness to adapt your diet and lifestyle, as well as your mental thought patterns.

If you are viewing this at home, set aside two hours, one day a week—preferably the same day each week— for the next eight weeks in order for this program to be the most beneficial. (For example: Monday 7–9 pm; Tuesday morning, 6–8 am.)

Also note that this program should be viewed as a mental health series concerned with educating and aiding individuals on the path to recovery.

There are also 8-week *Nedley Depression and Anxiety Recovery Programs™* available in the U.S. and other countries, facilitated by trained individuals. These programs are for the express purpose of mental health education. If you feel that participation in a hands-on experience with friendly coaches would be of additional benefit to you, then you should feel free to make arrangements to attend one of these programs.

The *Nedley Depression and Anxiety Recovery Program™* is not a substitute for a physician, psychiatrist, or a counselor, and if you are in need of help from such sources, you should not hesitate to seek it.

Nedley Health Solutions offers a Residential *Nedley Depression and Anxiety Recovery Program™*. For more information go to: **www.depressionthewayout.com.** This program is a full therapeutic program plus a certified educational program, utilizing physicians, licensed counselors, therapists, and other trained personnel.

For locations and to learn more, visit: **www.nedleydepressionrecovery.com**

About This Program

Due to the response from my book, *Depression: the Way Out*, and the success of the community Nedley Depression and Anxiety Recovery Program™—an eight-week series about overcoming depression and anxiety through lifestyle change—I receive more requests to speak than one person can handle. I decided that the best way to get this message of health to those who need it most would be to produce a recorded series of my live presentations along with the materials the participants receive. This allows any person, from the comfort of their home, to take advantage of the 20-Week Turn Around and find relief and happiness.

This workbook is designed to be used in connection with the DVD series and my book, *Depression: the Way Out*. I also recommend you take the comprehensive Nedley Depression and Anxiety Assessment Test (DAAT), either online or ask the person directing your 8-week program for a copy of the assessment. Make sure to include your full name, address, and date of birth. This will provide us with important data which will not only benefit you, but others who also suffer from this unfortunate and often debilitating disease.

Reading Prescriptions
These are designed to prepare you for the material included in the presentations (as well as to reinforce the ideas contained therein). Reading the prescribed chapters will allow you to have more familiarity with the concepts presented in each session, so you will benefit even more from Dr. Nedley's lectures.

Points from Dr. Nedley's Presentations
This will help you follow along more closely and take notes, as well as fill in the missing blanks on the slides in your book.

Lifestyle in Action
Bring forth Dr. Nedley's lessons into practical, easy to implement activities which can be incorporated into your own life in a fun, safe, and successful manner.

HOW TO IMPROVE YOUR BRAIN

1

DURING THIS SESSION YOU WILL LEARN:

What is depression or anxiety

Who is at risk

What contributes to depression or anxiety, and
is recovery possible

DETAILS OF THE HUMAN BRAIN

The most complicated structure ever investigated by science.

» 100 billion nerve _____ ✎ 1-a

» Even more supporting cells known as Glia

» Thousands of different types of neurons

DISORDERS OF THE BRAIN[1]

» 26.2% of Americans ages 15 and older—more than one in four adults—suffer from a diagnosable _____ ✎ 1-b disorder in any given year

DEPRESSION IS INCREASING[2, 3, 4]

» The number of people developing depression worldwide has steadily increased since 1915

» Major episodes of depression now occur frequently by age 25

» Overall risk of depression has _____ ✎ 1-c over time

LIFELONG RISK OF MAJOR DEPRESSION

» At least 1 in 4 _____ ✎ 1-d will suffer from major depression at some point in their lives

» At least 1 in 8 _____ ✎ 1-e will suffer from major depression at some point in their lives

» 99% of people will suffer from situational depression by age 70 as a result of serious loss

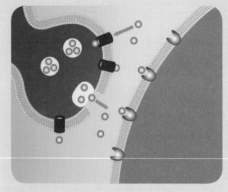

Synapse *is a region where nerve impulses are transmitted and received*

Purkinje cell *makes 200,000 connections with other cells*

_____

_____

_____

_____

_____

IMPACT OF MAJOR DEPRESSION[5]

» Affects up to 1 in 3 people who see an internal medicine physician

» Leading cause of _____ ✎ 1-f worldwide

» Costs an estimated $90 billion dollars in treatment, disability, and lost productivity in the United States each year

HOW CAN I KNOW IF IT'S MAJOR DEPRESSION?

If you experience at least 5 of the 9 symptoms for the majority of the time for at least 2 weeks, without recent obvious emotional trauma.

1. Deep sadness or emptiness
2. Apathy or loss of interest
3. Agitation or slowing down
4. Sleep disturbances
5. Weight or appetite changes
6. Lack of concentration
7. _____ ✎ 1-g
8. Feeling of worthlessness
9. Morbid thoughts

THE COST OF DEPRESSION[6]

» Lose an average of 5.6 hours of productive work per week

» 80% are impaired in daily functioning

» Less ability to concentrate, lower efficiency, and less ability to organize work

» More than twice as likely to take sick days

» In one study, the costs of absenteeism were directly related to taking antidepressant medication

» Depressed people are _____ ✎ 1-h more likely to become unemployed

Medications have their effect, but they have a limited effect. They are, by no means, a cure all for depression.

Severe Depression
Person has not recently faced obvious emotional trauma, but still experiences at least 5 of the 9 symptoms for at least two weeks.

Minor or Subsyndromal Depression
Person has not recently faced obvious emotional trauma, but still experiences at least 2 to 4 of the 9 symptoms for at least two weeks.

Situational Depression
Person has suffered a significant loss within the last 18 months and is experiencing depression symptoms.

THE LONG-TERM EFFECTS[7]

» Seven fewer weeks of work per year, a loss of 35% in lifetime income, and a lifetime loss of $300,000 for each family who has a depressed family member

» _____ ✎ 1-i loss (on average) of $10,400 per year in income by age 50

» The cost for the total group, over a lifetime, is 2.1 trillion dollars, which does not include the increased cost of medical care

MEDICAL BURDEN OF DEPRESSION[8, 9, 10, 11, 12]

» May cause a chronic _____ ✎ 1-j

» May cause osteoporosis

» Five times as likely to abuse drugs or alcohol

» Increases risk of developing asthma

» Increases stress hormone

» May increase problems with _____ ✎ 1-k or hostility

» Increases chance that offspring will suffer depression and physical medical problems

» Increases rate of decline in physical abilities with age

» Increases risk of lack of bladder control with age

» Decreases sex hormones

» Decreases CD8, increases IgA, decreases IgM, impairing immune system

» Decreases memory

» Decreases emotional intelligence and social pleasures

Whether you end up in a nursing home, as you age, has more to do with your mental health than your physical health.

MEDICAL BURDEN OF DEPRESSION INCLUDES DEATH[13, 14, 15, 16]

» Increases risk of stroke by 50%

» Increases risk of sudden death in heart attack survivors by 2½ times

» Increases risk of heart disease in men

» Increases risk of death from pneumonia

» Increases risk of suicide

WHAT ABOUT SUICIDE?[16, 17, 18]

» 8th leading cause of death in the U.S.

» 3rd leading cause of death in young people ages 10 to 24

» Twice as frequent as _____ ✎ 1-l

» Feelings of hopelessness is the best correlate of imminent suicidal action

» Other factors are impaired judgment or coping skills, impulsivity, isolation, history of mental illness

DEPRESSION

» Is a lifelong vulnerability for increasing millions of people

» Is a world economic crisis

» Is an _____ ✎ 1-m that is difficult

» The war on depression is winnable

» Eliminating depression and anxiety is possible

TREATING DEPRESSION

"Simply from a _____ ✎ 1-n point of view, effective treatment for depression makes economic sense. It's a good investment. If you effectively treat depression, people are more likely to work, require less disability coverage and— as cynical as it may sound—more likely to pay taxes. Treating depression pays. It's smart policy—and the right thing to do."

—ROBERT L. LEAHY, PH.D. AMERICAN INSTITUTE FOR COGNITIVE THERAPY

Depression and/or anxiety can be the cause of fibromyalgia, gastrointestinal upset, migraines, chronic pain, and a host of other conditions.

Antidepressants worsen impulsivity before they improve depression.

_____

_____

_____

_____

_____

_____

_____

_____

_____

CAUSES OF MAJOR DEPRESSION

» Myriads of causes:
  › Well over one hundred
  › Most fall into one of ten categories
» Depression and/or anxiety is most often a multifactorial disease.
  › Usually _____ 1-o categories of causes or more combined

THE TEN "HIT" CATEGORIES

1. _____ 1-p
2. Lifestyle
3. Circadian rhythm
4. Nutrition
5. Toxins
6. Social/inadequate coping/grief
7. Addiction
8. Medical condition
9. Developmental
10. Genetic

DON'T WAIT FOR DEPRESSION OR ANXIETY'S COMPLICATIONS

» Find out what hits (categories of causes) are impairing your brain
» Make the choice to eliminate the active reversible hits in your life
» Get ready for a far better, productive life, filled with far better decisions, better economics, and great life satisfaction

Have you taken your test to determine your "hit" categories?

_____
_____
_____
_____
_____
_____
_____
_____
_____
_____
_____
_____
_____

HOW TO IMPROVE YOUR BRAIN, part 2

IS THERE MORE THAT CAN BE DONE?

» Searched the medical literature

» Etiology

» Diagnosing major depression and prescribing an antidepressant is akin to seeing a patient with a chief complaint of swollen feet and diagnosing "swollen foot syndrome" and prescribing a diuretic

MAJOR DEPRESSION–CONSTELLATION OF SYMPTOMS

» The diagnosis does not give any indication to the cause of the disease

» If we want to increase the likelihood of a long-term solution, we must identify the causes of depression and systematically treat them

» Unfortunately, this is not as simple a process as prescribing a drug

» Like most chronic diseases, depression is a multifactorial disease

» The most effective treatments will be based on an all-fronts attack on as many causes identified to be operative

It is important to find the cause in order to find the cure.

THE FRONTAL LOBE

» Scientific studies show the frontal lobe is the seat of:

» _____ 🔧 1-q

» Morality

» The will

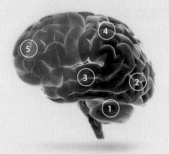

RESEARCH IN THE LAST 15 YEARS

It is now well established that one of the main characteristics of virtually all depressed individuals—no matter what the underlying cause—is a significant decrease in the frontal lobe's _____ 🔧 1-r and activity.

EFFECTS OF A COMPROMISED FRONTAL LOBE

» Impairment of moral principle

» Lack of foresight

» Abstract reasoning impaired

» Mathematical understanding diminished

» Loss of _____ 🔧 1-s

» Lack of restraint

INADEQUATE WATER INTAKE[19, 20, 21, 22]

» Difficulty in staying focused

» Impaired short-term _____ 🔧 1-t function

» Impaired recall of long-term memory

» Diminished ability to perform mental arithmetic

» Mental fatigue

» Headache

» Depressed mood

1. **Cerebellum:** coordination, graceful athleticism, precision in movement, balance.

2. **Occipital lobe:** makes sense of visual information so that we are able to understand it, architectural skills, and spatial orientation (like a 3-D map) of objects in the visual field.

3. **Temporal lobe:** memory, auditory processing, vocabulary, and musical ability.

4. **Parietal lobe:** sensation, speech, language comprehension, attention, and calculations.

5. **Frontal lobe:** reasoning, planning, movement, creative problem solving, higher forms of math and creative speech, spirituality, the will, and where emotional intelligence and general intelligence come together.

MODERATE DEHYDRATION IN TEENS[23]

"Given the limited availability of brain metabolic resources, these findings suggest that prolonged states of _____ 1-u water intake adversely impact executive functions such as planning and visual-spatial processing."

HYPNOSIS

» Hypnosis attempts to cancel out frontal lobe functions and bring people into a trance in which they are highly suggestible

» This is most easily accomplished by training the eyes to focus in on one object, the best object being a little flickering light

» The person will record information and duties without interpretation, or without frontal lobe activity

SCIENCE AND TELEVISION

» Increases daydreaming

» Decreases creative ingenuity

» Decreases interest in reading

» Decreases interest in learning

» Reduces _____ 1-v

» Trains in non-reaction

» Increases aggressiveness

» Reduces sensitivity to violence

» Addictive

TAKES AWAY PRECIOUS TIME FOR

» _____ 1-w

» Achievement

» Spiritual pursuits

Depressed   Recovered

Notice the greatest improvement of blood flow is in the frontal lobe

It takes 30 years for the frontal lobe to develop.

Empathy
Ability to understand what someone else is going through, even though you have never been through it yourself.

MUSIC

» Music enters the brain through its _____ 1-x regions, which include the temporal lobe and limbic system

» From there, some kinds of music tend to produce a frontal lobe response that influences the will, moral worth, and reasoning power

CONSTANT STIMULATION OF THE SENSES

"Constant stimulation of the senses shuts down the analytical processes, and ultimately shuts down the ability to face life rationally. This leads to escape techniques that involve withdrawal, apathy, and rejection of disciplined thinking when faced with difficult duties and decisions."

—ALVIN TOFFLER

CHARACTERISTIC'S OF BRAIN OPTIMIZING MUSIC

» _____ 1-y

» Can be simple, yet attractive

» Beautiful non-dissonance harmonies

» Straight rhythms

» March rhythms

» Rhythm less prominent than melody and harmony

» Music tells a story

MUSIC THERAPY LIFTS MOOD[23]

Music psychotherapy, in which people are encouraged to reflect on their past, present, and future while listening to classical music, improves mood and reduces stress.

» Six sessions of classical music therapy were held over a 12-week period in 23 to 45 year-olds

Rapid Scene of Reference
During an entertainment television program the scene of reference changes on average every 3 seconds.

Your frontal lobe circulation begins to go down after 90 seconds to 3 minutes of viewing rapid changes in scene reference, so that you are no longer able to critically analyze content.

» These subjects showed:

> › Improved scores on test of overall mood

> › Reported feeling less depressed

> › Reported feeling less fatigue

> › Cortisol levels improved (dropped)

ENHANCING FRONTAL LOBE FUNCTION

» Analytical thinking

» Working with your hands

» Analyzing and enjoying melodious music

» Contemplating or creating proverbs

» Reading, analyzing, and comparing scripture

ESSENTIALLY ONLY TWO CATEGORIES OF PEOPLE

» Those who know someone with a mental disorder

» Those who have a mental disorder themselves

DON'T WAIT FOR DEPRESSION'S COMPLICATIONS

» Get on the best pathway to health of mind

» Make the choices that will positively impact your life long-term

» Complete and implement the *Nedley Depression and Anxiety Recovery Program*™

Anything that suppresses the frontal lobe can be addictive.

Appropriate music therapy improves the flow of blood to the frontal lobe even if you don't suffer from depression.

Music therapy is well established to be a primary modality in enhancing frontal lobe function to help with anxiety and depression.

⚙ What You Learned

» The war on depression is winnable

» Music therapy lifts the mood

» Adequate water intake improves mental health

Reading Prescription

» *Depression: the Way Out,* chapters 1, 2, and 3

» Chapter in the book of Proverbs that corresponds with each day's date

» *SOS Help for Emotions: Managing Anxiety, Anger and Depression,* chapters 1, 2, and 3

LIFESTYLE IN ACTION

Master the Process of Intentional Thinking

What we converse about can influence the positive or negative direction of our health. The following exercise will greatly benefit you if you dedicate yourself to succeeding.

For two weeks—14 consecutive days—decide to say nothing critical or negative about anything or any person. In this exercise, not one critical word is allowed to be spoken to others (not even "constructive" criticism). This may seem impossible for those raising children or leading others in a business environment, but realize that expectations and consequences can still be enforced without critical words.

Speak to others using positive words and thoughts, or speak nothing at all! If you slip up on any day during the two weeks, you must begin counting again until you achieve all 14 consecutive days. Don't get discouraged if you have to start over; it gets easier as you become more aware of your thoughts. Remember, this program is eight weeks long! Virtually everyone will be able to do it by week eight.

Championship athletes do it, CEO's do it, and you, too, can master the process of intentional thinking!

Making Gratitude Part of Every Day

When you focus on being thankful for the small things in life, you learn to see the positive and emphasize those feelings. Take time to notice the blade of green grass or the blue sky. Appreciate kind interactions like someone letting you be first in line or the receptionist's smile directed at you. Recognize the tangible, beneficial way you are affected by the dog's obvious excitement when you arrive home. As you concentrate on the positive, the negative, discontented thoughts more easily vanish.

By recording circumstances that have touched you in a positive way, underlining the experiences that bring you satisfaction and joy, you learn not to become discouraged when situations appear overwhelming and helpless.

It is not natural to be thankful. We teach our children to say thank you and write cards expressing gratitude. Retrain your thoughts to cultivate a state of mind that is appreciative and grateful, and you will benefit significantly. You will feel calmer, more positive, and it will be easier to have a smile on your face. Others will notice, ponder, and more often than not, respond in a similar manner.

Action Step 1.1 — Gratitude List

List 5 things that you are grateful for (people, experiences, or things):

1. _____

2. _____

3. _____

4. _____

5. _____

Note: *use a notebook and begin a gratitude journal.*

" *Gratitude unlocks the fullness of life. It turns what we have into enough, and more. It turns denial into acceptance, chaos into order, confusion to clarity. It can turn a meal into a feast, a house into a home, a stranger into a friend.*

—MELODY BEATTIE

" *Nothing tends more to promote health of body and of soul than does a spirit of gratitude and praise.*

—MINISTRY OF HEALING 251

Tune up Your Mind and Tune in to Music

Listening to classical music has been scientifically proven to help relieve stress, anxiety, and depression. The calming power of music has a relaxing effect on the mind and body. It also has a beneficial effect on physiological functions like slowing the pulse and heart rate, lowering blood pressure, and decreasing levels of stress hormones.

Remember to listen to classical music or traditional church hymns daily while driving, cleaning house, at the office, or at live concerts.

It is important to note that not every type of music can qualify for this activity. The classical music you select should be more traditional and less experimental or strange. Albinoni, Bach, Beethoven, Brahms, Handel, Mozart, Respighi, Tchaikovsky and Vivaldi are a few of the composers you can choose from. Also remember that as you begin this regular exercise of the mind, it is not important that you like classical music. You will benefit from it regardless of your tastes in music, and you will find it more enjoyable over time.

Action Step 1.2   Classical Music

At least every two weeks, listen intently to classical music for forty-five minutes to one hour. It will lift your mood and establish good mental clarity.

While listening, pay attention to the music and reflect upon your life. Thinking about how you would like your future to be different from your past, or just taking stock of the good things and relationships in your life can be excellent examples. As you listen to music, allow it to speak to you. Do you see in your "mind's eye" a nature scene, a story line?

Set a date to complete the listening activity: _____

Write your thoughts while listening: _____

_____

_____

Hydrate Before It's Too Late

Adequate hydration is crucial for optimal function of both brain and body. Dehydration can occur easily and imperceptibly when drinking enough water is not prioritized. Signs can include lack of concentration, fatigue, or headache. Consider the implications of not drinking enough water by reviewing the results of dehydration from the lecture notes.

Action Step 1.3 — Water Intake Formula

Formula:
$$\frac{\text{Weight (lb)}}{2} = \text{Water (oz/day)}$$

Formula:
$$\text{Weight (kg)} \times 30 \text{ (ml)} = \text{Water (L/day)}$$

Example:
$$\frac{160 \text{ (lb)}}{2} = 80 \text{ (oz/day)}$$

Example:
$$75 \text{ (kg)} \times 30 \text{ (ml)} = 2.25 \text{ (L/day)}$$

You:
$$\frac{\_\_\_\_ \text{ (lb)}}{2} = \_\_\_\_ \text{ (oz/day)}$$

You:
$$\_\_\_\_ \text{ (kg)} \times 30 \text{ (ml)} = \_\_\_\_ \text{ (L/day)}$$

Tips for Success: *Set your goal for the day. For example, 20 oz (600ml) before breakfast, 30 oz (900 ml) before lunch, and 30 oz (900 ml) before dinner, to ensure you complete your goal for the day (1 cup = 8 oz).*

(⬭) cups (before breakfast)　　(⬭) cups (before lunch)　　(⬭) cups (afternoon)

Note: *This is only an estimate. The actual requirement may vary depending on many factors like: pregnancy, breast feeding, morbid or gross obesity, exercise, high altitude and other medical conditions. Unless kidney failure, the recommended minimum water intake should be 6 glasses or 48 oz (1420ml) per day.*

Our blood is also greatly affected by not getting enough water. It circulates through the body and the brain a lot better when it's not thick and sluggish. All this results in better overall body and brain health. Drink generous quantities of fresh, pure water between your meals each day. "Water substitutes" don't count; caffeinated and other beverages can actually cause the body to expel fluids. Athletes and outdoor workers should be extra diligent, because their activities can place them at higher risk for impaired performances due to dehydration.

Action Step 1.4 — Signs of Dehydration

Mark what applies to you:

1. Fatigue, brain fog ○
2. Urine appears dark or amber ○
3. Sudden lightheadedness or dizziness ○
4. Increased heart rate or palpitations ○
5. Overheated ○
6. Muscle cramps or spasms ○
7. Constipation ○
8. Loss of skin elasticity ○
9. Going more than 4 hours without a bathroom break ○
10. Muscle cramps or spasms, dry mouth, or dry eyes ○

Boost Your Mood with Exercise

Exercise increases circulation and brain function and regulates mood helping you to feel and think better. Physical exercise can take many forms, but as long as it gets your body moving and your blood pumping, it will benefit your depression.

Raising your heart rate will help you to process a large amount of oxygen, increase your energy level, and help you feel great. The sing-talk test is a good way to test if you are exercising too hard or not enough. Here's an easy way to tell—if you can't talk while exercising, you're working too hard. If you can sing, step up the pace.

Many people who have not previously used exercise as a fitness tool are afraid to start. There may be legitimate concerns. If you have a heart condition or at risk for one, check with your physician before beginning an intense exercise program.

Action Step 1.5	**Exercise List**

Choose an exercise from the list below and start today. Begin your exercise program for at least 60 minutes a day (may divide this into two thirty minute sessions).

1. Jogging	◯
2. Hiking	◯
3. Bicycling	◯
4. Brisk walking (try actively swinging your arms, too)	◯
5. Aerobics	◯
6. Tennis or racquetball	◯
7. Swimming	◯
8. Ice or roller skating or roller blading (in-line skating)	◯
9. Vigorous gardening	◯
10. Other:	◯

Getting Started: Without commitment, nothing gets done. Put your goal in writing. Post it where it will be a daily reminder.

📅 Organize Your Life

When you are organized, it allows you to feel more relaxed and happy. Being organized can also have a positive effect on your health, reducing stress and boosting your immune system.

Checklists can be very helpful in staying organized. Use this example checklist to help you get organized as you move through this program. Write your routines on a piece of paper in the order that they need to be done. This is a start, and a goal to work toward. Place a notebook that holds your routines on your kitchen counter, or try putting it in a sheet protector that can be checked off with a dry erase marker and can be wiped clean at the end of the day.

Morning Routine Example:

- ○ Set a wake-up time
- ○ Make the bed
- ○ Get dressed for exercise
- ○ Drink water
- ○ Sit by your light therapy box
- ○ Read your chapter of Proverbs
- ○ Exercise
- ○ Sort laundry, load washer so it is ready to start after work (or set timer for late afternoon)
- ○ Take shower
- ○ Grooming
- ○ Start preparing breakfast
- ○ Empty dishwasher
- ○ Pack lunch (plan to eat it outside in the sun if possible)
- ○ Feed pets
- ○ Take medications and vitamins
- ○ Eat breakfast (make sure to get your omega-3's)
- ○ Brush teeth
- ○ Fill in the *Healthy Lifestyle Scorecard*
- ○ Check e-mail
- ○ Listen to classical music while driving to work

Evening Routine Example:

- ○ Eat a light supper (optional)
- ○ Clean off dining table, do dishes
- ○ Start laundry
- ○ Open mail
- ○ Take a stroll around the block with your family while deep breathing
- ○ Reduce water intake by 6 pm to decrease bathroom visits at night
- ○ Pick up and put away obvious clutter
- ○ Put clothes and shoes away / lay out clothes for tomorrow
- ○ Turn off technology
- ○ Pull covers back, get family ready for bed
- ○ Plan your next day
- ○ Fill in the *Healthy Lifestyle Scorecard*
- ○ Write in your gratitude journal
- ○ Brush teeth/clean face
- ○ Read for a while
- ○ Fall asleep with a smile on your face and in your heart

Healthy Lifestyle Scorecard — Sample

DAILY ACTIVITIES	SUNDAY	MONDAY
1. AVOID NEGATIVE SPEECH	✔	12:00-8:00pm
2. CLASSICAL MUSIC	6:30-7:15pm _music therapy_	7:30-8:00am _on the way to work_
3. WATER | HYDRO	5:30am 8oz, 8:15am 12oz, 11:00am 16oz, 1:30pm 8oz, 3:00pm 16oz, 6:15pm 8oz ✔	5:30am 16oz, 8:00am 16oz, 10:30am 8oz, 1:00pm 8oz, 3:00pm 16oz, 6:00pm 8oz ✔✔
4. EXERCISE	6:15-7:15am	_total: 1h 20min_
5. SLEEP	9:30pm - 3:15am	9:30pm - 12:00am; 3:30am - 5:30am
6. DEEP BREATHING	6:15-7:15am	7:30-8:00am
7. LIGHT THERAPY	5:40-6:10am	5:40-6:40am
8. PROVERBS	_Proverbs 17, 5:40-6:10am, verse 22_	_Proverbs 18, 5:40-6:10am, verse 15_
9. OMEGA-3	_2 tablespoons ground flax seed_	_2 tablespoons ground chia seed_
10. GRATITUDE	_1. sunshine: warms me up 2. fresh air: calms me down 3. clean water: I am refreshed_	_1. spring: new life 2. family: love & support 3. job: support my family_

The Healthy Lifestyle Scorecard includes ten categories that are important to your recovery. For each category make a daily entry.

Use the Healthy Lifestyle Scorecard to keep track of how you're doing on the different parts of the Nedley Depression and Anxiety Recovery Program™. You can write your answers in the book (beginning on p.148), copy or photocopy it onto another sheet, or use a dry-erase board if that is easier for you. The success rate of this program is higher for those who comply with filling in the scorecard. You may choose to perform multiple activities concurrently.

1. **AVOID NEGATIVE SPEECH:** Mark days or hours in which you avoided negative speech.
2. **CLASSICAL MUSIC:** Note the time you listened to classical music daily. Remember the music therapy session (see _Action Step 1.2_).
3. **WATER:** Total number of ounces/mL you drank throughout the day and what time you drank them. Also check mark if you included hydrotherapy into daily routine (once or twice daily).
4. **EXERCISE:** Record the beginning and ending time for all exercise sessions. If multiple exercise sessions, enter the total time.
5. **SLEEP:** Track sleeping patterns for each night. Note any times that you woke up during the night and the approximate time you went back to sleep.
6. **DEEP BREATHING:** Write down any time you practiced deep breathing (fresh air) throughout the day (including during exercise, while doing classical music therapy, etc.).
7. **LIGHT THERAPY:** Total light therapy sessions with light box or natural outdoor light.
8. **PROVERBS/SPIRITUAL ACTIVITY:** Record chapter(s) read in Proverbs, time, and favorite verse.
9. **OMEGA-3:** Aim for 3,000 mg at the beginning of the day. Any additional omega-3 throughout the day is a bonus!
10. **GRATITUDE:** List three things you are thankful for and why.

LIFESTYLE THERAPIES FOR DEPRESSION AND ANXIETY

2

DURING THIS SESSION YOU WILL LEARN:

The signs and symptoms of anxiety

What we can change about ourselves and what to expect when we do

The importance of dwelling on the good

GENERALIZED ANXIETY DISORDER

Indicated by three or more of the following symptoms:

1. Feeling wound-up, tense, or restless
2. Easily becoming fatigued or worn-out
3. Concentration problems
4. Irritability
5. Significant tension in muscles
6. Difficulty with sleep

» Excessive anxiety and worry (with a decrease in ability to function) about a variety of events and situations

» Difficulty in _____ ✎ 2-a the worry

» Unable to control, cope, or relax

OTHER FORMS OF ANXIETY

» Panic disorder

» Agoraphobia

› Anxiety about places or situations from which escape might be difficult, or in which you might feel trapped, helpless, or embarrassed

» Social anxiety or social phobia

» Obsessive compulsive disorder

» _____ ✎ 2-b stress disorder

» Post traumatic stress disorder

» Specific phobias

A lot of therapies for depression can also work for anxiety.

_____
_____
_____
_____
_____
_____
_____
_____
_____
_____
_____
_____
_____
_____
_____
_____

MEDICATION[1]

» Drugs are the most common treatment for depression and anxiety

» 51% of patients will experience an improvement in their mood or other symptoms

» Less than 20% of patients on anti-depressants feel they are "cured" or back to normal while taking the medication

THE OTHER SIDE OF THE COIN[2, 3]

» Up to 30% do not improve with any medication

» 50% report bothersome side effects

» Over half of these quit taking their medication

» Two-thirds are not very satisfied with their treatment

» 75% on those on medication state that depression continues to _____ ✎ 2-c their social life and their work performance, as well as affect family life

RELAPSE RATES

» Those who discontinue usage after 3 months have a 77% relapse rate within 2 years

» Another study showed a 40% relapse rate within a year

» Even those who continue medication have a relapse rate of 20-40%

MEDICATIONS MAY HAVE THEIR PLACE

» Can help if not used as an ultimate solution

» Reserved for _____ ✎ 2-d to severe depression and/or anxiety

» Definite goal should be discontinuation within 6 months to a year in most cases

» If this program is carried out, expect a 90% success rate in withdrawal without relapse

LIFESTYLE HITS

» Not on a _____ ✎ 2-e exercise program

» Not regularly being exposed to daylight at least 30 minutes a day

» Rarely breathing fresh air

TAKING LONG WALKS[4]

» Taking long brisk walks is beneficial in reducing depression and anxiety

» Hour-long walks are good

» 7 days minimum are needed for positive results in most cases of depression

DEPRESSION AND PHYSICAL EXERCISE[5, 6]

» Need a minimum of 17.5 calories/kg/week to produce a measurable response

» Need a minimum of 30 minutes of brisk treadmill walking per day for 10 days to begin to show a positive mental health response

» 16 weeks of aerobic fitness training has an antidepressant response equivalent to Zoloft, but with _____ ✎ 2-f relapse

CBT
Cognitive-behavioral therapy attempts to help us recognize how our thoughts influence our emotions and behavior. CBT trains people to think rationally.

Success in any line demands a definite goal.

Anxiety can actually be reduced the first time you go out to exercise.

ANXIETY AND PHYSICAL EXERCISE[7, 8]

» There is no doubt that aerobic exercise training is anxiety-relieving in healthy volunteers

» In addition, studies on healthy subjects and multiple case reports reveal that an acute bout of exercise relieves anxiety

» Generalized anxiety disorder, social phobia, and/or panic disorder respond to aerobic _____ 🔑 2-g training especially when combined with CBT

» Panic disorder responds to both aerobic and muscle building exercise

» Post-traumatic stress disorder can also respond to exercise training

BECOMING FIT THROUGH INTERVAL TRAINING

» Mixes rest with exercise

» Accelerates fitness to a high level in a shorter time period

» Ideal for both the unfit and the _____ 🔑 2-h

» Less muscle soreness

» Thyroid function improves

INTERVAL TRAINING

» Exercise vigorously to achieve desired heart rate

» When heart rate reaches the upper limit, rest

» When heart rate drops to the lower limit, resume vigorous exercise

Interval Training (I.T.) Formula

$$IC \times (HR_{max} - RHR) + RHR = THR$$

(IC)	Intensity Constant training
(HR_{max})	Maximal Heart Rate = 220 – age
(RHR)	Resting Heart Rate
(THR)	Target Heart Rate zone

Resting Heart Rate

Heart rate can be recorded on the inside of the wrist (radial pulse; preferred) or on the neck to the side of the windpipe (carotid pulse; use with caution). To gather an accurate recording, it is best to record the resting HR on rising in the morning. Test your resting heart rate three mornings in a row and average the three readings.

Intensity Constant Training

Beginner: constant 0.4

Intermediate: constant 0.5

Advanced: constant 0.6

Example:

A 45-year-old person with a desired intensity training of 60% (constant 0.6) of his heart rate maximum. If this 45-year-old person has a resting heart rate of 80 bpm, then the formula would be solved as follows:

220 – 45 (age) = 175 HR_{max}

175 – 80 (RHR) = 95

95 x 0.6 = 57

57 + 80 = 137 bpm

Thus, 137 beats per minute is the target heart rate.

In I.T. it is desirable to exercise within a 10 beat range. So in this example the range would be 132-142. Above 142, slow down your exercise, below 132 speed up your exercise.

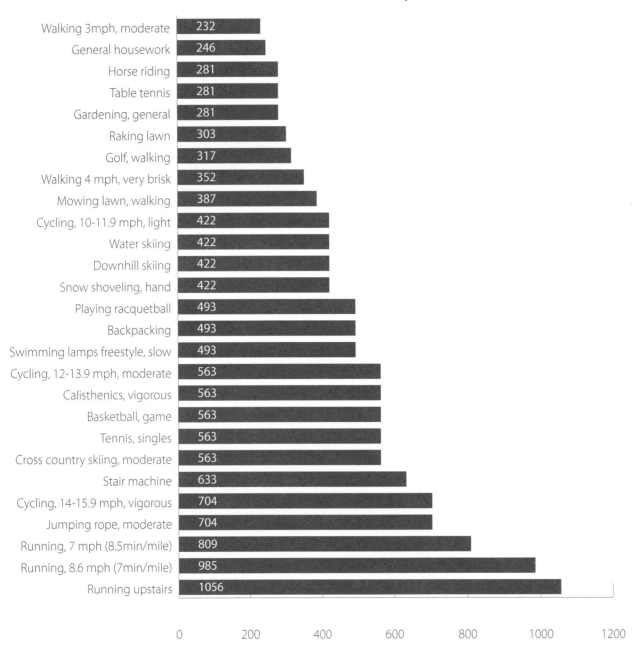

Calories Burned Per Hour (155 lbs. person)

LIFESTYLE THERAPIES FOR DEPRESSION AND ANXIETY, part 2

BRIGHT LIGHT THERAPY[9]

- » Light is needed for adequate _____ ⚷ 2-i production
- » Possibly best upon or before awakening
- » Works best for those that also are fatigued or have a tendency to eat or sleep too much, or have winter depression
- » Effective for partum and postpartum depression
- » 10,000 lux white light boxes 30-60 minutes/day, or 460 nm blue light

WINTER DEPRESSION[10]

- » 96 patients were randomized to receive light therapy plus a placebo capsule or placebo light therapy plus Prozac (20 mg/day) for 8 weeks
- » The clinical response rate in each group was 67%
- » Further analysis indicated that light therapy provided a quicker initial improvement

BENEFITS OF FRESH AIR[11]

_____ ⚷ 2-j ions present in:

- » Moving ocean surf
- » Waterfalls or moving water
- » Following a thunderstorm
- » Evergreen trees
- » Improves learning and concentration

Circadian Rhythm
Sleep/wake cycle in our 24-hour rhythm.

Truly the light is sweet, and a pleasant thing it is for the eyes to behold the sun.
—ECCLESIASTES 11:7

» Reduces anxiety

» Improves mood

Researchers found that among more than 300,000 Dutch adults and children, those living near more "green spaces" tended to have lower rates of _____ ✎ 2-k different health conditions. The link was especially strong when it came to depression and anxiety.

HEALTHY LUNGS, HEALTHY BRAIN[12]

» For children, healthy lungs may mean healthier scores on tests of memory, learning, and intelligence

» Researchers at Harvard University examined data on 165 Boston children who had been followed since birth

» At the age of 6, the children had their lung function tested. At age 9, they completed standard tests of memory, learning ability and intelligence.

» The researchers found that for each increase in the children's lung-function performance, there was a corresponding increase in their cognitive-test scores

CIRCADIAN RHYTHM HITS

» Regular insomnia

» Sleeping more than 9 hours a day routinely

» Sleeping less than 6 hours a day routinely

» "Shift" work

» Not having regular hours for sleeping and eating

After a thunderstorm go outside and take a deep breath.

Practice taking six breathes a minute, deeply.

✎

_____

_____

_____

_____

_____

_____

_____

_____

_____

_____

_____

_____

_____

DEPRESSION AND INSOMNIA

» Ironically, the depression seems to clear and the energy level improves as the person stays awake

» Going to bed late or "sleep deprivation" is a _____ ✎ 2-I treatment for "circadian rhythm" depression

» Once sleep occurs, the depression returns causing the person to not want to get up or be a "zombie" in the morning

TREATMENT

» Awaken with the sun, or be exposed to at least 30 minutes of bright light starting immediately upon awakening

» _____ ✎ 2-m hours for sleeping, eating, and exercise

» Requires an alarm clock at first

» Sleep's three factors:
  › No noise
  › Be still
  › Eyes closed

RESEARCH[13]

» Researchers found that men who were exposed to an hour of bright light first thing in the morning experienced an increase in luteinizing hormone (LH)

» LH influences reproductive hormones in both men and women. Increases in LH in men drive up testosterone levels, while the hormone triggers ovulation in women.

» Studies have shown that LH may help with depression. It can improve _____ ✎ 2-n and there may be a muscle-building and strengthening effect.

» When women with long and irregular menstrual cycles were exposed to bright light, the cycles regularized

When you are sleep deprived, your brain starts to dump serotonin in uncontrolled ways.

Look for the good tired feeling at the end of the day.

_____
_____
_____
_____
_____
_____
_____
_____
_____
_____
_____

AVOID PESSIMISM[14]

» 224 subjects were studied as to their degree of optimism and pessimism

» Pessimism predicted:

  › Anxiety

  › Perceived stress

  › Physical disease

  › Optimism predicted nothing

THE ZURICH AXIOMS

» Optimism means expecting the best, but confidence means knowing how to handle the worst

» Never make a move if you are merely optimistic

DWELL ON THE GOOD

» Avoid pessimism

» Not permitted to say anything critical about anyone or anything for 14 consecutive days (2 weeks)

» Once something critical is said, begin the 14 days over again

» "Nothing tends more to promote health of body and of soul than does a spirit of gratitude and praise."

—MINISTRY OF HEALING 251

While the power of positive thinking is encouraged as a way to improve health and well being, this study shows it is more important to avoid negative thinking.

It is a positive duty to resist melancholy, discontented thoughts and feelings.

—ELLEN WHITE

What we talk about, and what we allow our mind to dwell on, does play a significant role in regard to our future mental health.

⚙ What You Learned

» Breathing exercises can improve health and aid mental clarity

» Early morning sunlight is best for improving mood

» You can take control of your life by improving your lifestyle

Reading Prescription

» *Depression: the Way Out,* chapter 5

» Chapter in the book of Proverbs that corresponds with each day's date

» *SOS Help for Emotions: Managing Anxiety, Anger and Depression,* chapters 4–6

» *Telling Yourself the Truth,* chapters 1–3

LIFESTYLE IN ACTION

Take a Deep Breath

Conscious breathing can relieve stress and reduce anxiety, increase vitality, and help eliminate depression. Impaired breathing can aggravate the anxiety and depression a person may already experience. Scientific studies show that when the oxygen levels in the body (especially blood and brain) are lower than optimum, the mood is adversely affected. Pure air improves muscle function, mental power, and exercise tolerance. It is important to keep your oxygen levels high.

One very effective way to accomplish this is through deep breathing exercises. Better oxygen levels are reached during deep breathing at three to six breaths per minute. To prevent shortness of breath while breathing six times per minute it is necessary to breathe very deeply. This not only improves blood oxygen levels during the time of exercise, but also throughout the entire day!

Action Step 2.1 — Deep Breathing

Your goal is to spend 30–45 minutes each day taking no more than six complete breaths each minute. Divide the time into two or three sessions if you need to, but be sure to get the total time each day. You will notice tremendous benefits from this exercise!

1. Stand erect with proper posture.

2. Inhale slowly and deeply through your nose for 5 seconds, focusing on the air going in while your diaphragm expands. This ensures that the diaphragm is pulling air into the bases of the lungs.

3. Then exhale slowly through your mouth for 5 seconds, focusing on the air going out while your diaphragm contracts.

4. Repeat steps 2 and 3 aiming for 3 to 6 breaths per minute.

   Total time in breathing exercise: ( ) min/day

Action Step 2.2 — Balloon Exercise

Imagine that your diaphragm area is a balloon, getting bigger when your breathe in, and getting smaller when you breathe out. With this in mind, practice blowing up an actual balloon which encourages you to contract your diaphragm and core muscles.

1. Stand up straight with shoulders back.

2. Inhale through your nose and exhale through your mouth into the balloon.
   Remember there are two "balloons" you are filling–your diaphragm area and the balloon. When you take a deep breath you are filling your lungs and when you exhale you are filling the balloon.

3. Repeat until there is always one "balloon" filled!

Brighten Your Day, Flip the Switch

If you feel moody or haven't been sleeping well, it may be time to see yourself in a new light, literally. Light helps regulate the natural rhythms of our body and mind, and not getting enough or the right kind of light can impact our health. Sufficient bright light exposure is therefore critical for all those suffering from depression.

A study included 89 men and women who were randomly assigned to one of two groups. In one, participants were given a light-therapy box that emitted pale blue light identical to the blue-light box recommended by *Nedley Health Solutions*. They used it every morning for one hour over three weeks. The other group were given boxes that emitted a dim red light, which has no known benefits or harm to the body or the brain.

Three weeks after the therapy ended, more people in the blue light-therapy group were considered treatment "responders"—meaning their depression scores had dropped by at least 50%. Of the light-therapy patients, 58% were responders, versus 34% of the control group.

Patients who underwent light therapy began to show a steeper rise in evening levels of the hormone melatonin, which promotes sleep. They also had a healthy drop in levels of the "stress hormone" cortisol—which, at the start of the study, had been elevated. According to some psychiatrists this study shows that light therapy definitely should have a role in treating depression.[15]

Bright light therapy can also help restore the normal daily body rhythm called circadian rhythm. If a person has a difficult time getting up in the morning or considers himself to be a night person, chances are very good that there is a problem with the circadian rhythm.

Setting Your Body Clock

To properly reset your circadian rhythm you need to get 30-60 minutes of daily exposure to bright light within 10 minutes of your normal wake time. For example, if you want to wake up daily at 6 am, you need to be exposed to bright light no later than 6:10 am for 30-60 minutes.

Ways to Get Light Exposure:

» Create a natural light box. Find a sunny spot in your home and sit there while reading the newspaper, having breakfast, or practicing your breathing.

» Use a medical-grade light box. It has a similar effect on the mood as a sunny blue sky. Outdoor daylight is approximately 15 times brighter than normal indoor lighting. So, if you cannot enjoy natural daylight upon awakening, it will be necessary to purchase a light therapy box.

General Tips:

1. Do not focus directly on the light source, whether natural or artificial. For the artificial light box, it is best to have it 20 degrees off from your straight ahead gaze.

2. Insomnia or unwanted early morning waking (for instance 1:30 or 2:30 am) can be corrected by bright light exposure for 30 minutes in mid-to-late afternoon.

3. You can combine bright light therapy with outdoor exercise, reading, or listening to classical music. For instance, walk outdoors while listening to classical music on headphones or read in front of your light box.

4. On purchasing a light box: for effective therapy, boxes vary in terms of distance one must be from the light source—some may need to be held near your face; others are intended for use within 16-24 inches. There are some companies that sell medical-grade light therapy boxes. Check *www.nedleyhealthsolutions.com* for an option.

Action Step 2.3 — Light Therapy to Reset Circadian Rhythm

This week get exposure to outdoor light (or bright light from a therapy box) for at least 30-60 minutes per day. What time have you set as your wake up time? _____ When will you get your bright light therapy? _____

Improve Blood Flow with Massage

One of the values of massage is its action on the circulatory system. The amount of stress and tension created by modern lifestyles and schedules cause increased tension in the muscles of the upper back and neck. As a result, pain and headaches may occur, affecting mental performance. Massage combined with other treatments can be used profitably in nervous and emotional disorders. In order for a massage to be most effective, it should take about an hour. However, even a brief massage can do a small amount of good.

Although the exact mechanism is not known, therapeutic massage is beneficial for a variety of ailments by promoting relaxation. Physiological measures such as heart rate, respiratory rate and blood pressure decrease from baseline during massage, providing further evidence of its relaxing properties.

Good massages teach relaxation in general, as well. Through awareness of muscle tension, posture can improve. Imagine a forward-leaning, stooped posture being corrected. A new, erect back posture increases the rib cage size, so lung capacity is increased and more air is exchanged. This in turn increases the amount of oxygen carried by the vessels to the brain, so that frontal lobe function may be enhanced.

Action Step 2.4   Massage

Do a quick self-massage for decreasing tension:

» Sit in a relaxed position.

» Take your hand and place it on the opposite shoulder.

» Press your fingers firmly (like typing) as you move from the sleeve seam up the neck to the ear level.

» Do this on each shoulder several times throughout the day.

Stimulating Contrast Showers

Hydrotherapy, the therapeutic use of water, has been used successfully for centuries to treat a number of physical and mental ailments. The application of appropriate hot and cold baths to relieve depressive symptoms is very effective, safe, and easy—and free from adverse side effects and expense.

For those who are severely depressed, this treatment must be done two times a day for seven to ten days. Once the depression improves, decrease the treatment to once each day. When no depression is present, three treatments per week should be done for at least six months.

When using this method of treatment, the same precautions should be observed as when preparing for a vigorous exercise program. Persons with advanced heart disease, serious blood pressure problems, advanced diabetes with neuropathy, or other serious health conditions should not use contrast showers, unless approved by their physician.

The hot water should not exceed 107 °F coming from the tap (no more than 104 °F in a tub). Your water heater has a control that allows you to adjust it so that it will not exceed the set temperature. Before doing this treatment you can check the maximum temperature that your shower will reach by adjusting the faucet so that only hot water is flowing, measuring with a thermometer. This will help you to avoid scalding, and aid in peace of mind knowing that the water will not be dangerously hot. The cold water should be no colder than 55°F.

For Best Results Follow These Steps:

1. Gradually adjust the shower temperature as warm as your skin will allow for 3-5 minutes.

2. Turn the faucet to cold while vigorously rinsing your entire body for 30 seconds.

3. Turn the water back to hot for 3 minutes. Cold for 30 seconds.

4. Repeat step 3 making sure you end with cold. This is breathtaking, but refreshing!

5. Towel-dry and dress to keep warm and comfortable.

6. Rest in a reclined position for 20 minutes. This is important because your body has been stimulated and needs to rest properly to receive full benefit from the treatment.

   Hint: *place a timer in a water-tight plastic bag to use while in the shower.*

Salt Glow

This is another modality to increase circulation, resulting in improved blood flow to the brain.

Choose a bowl large enough to hold one cup of table salt (vary the salt coarseness to your desire). Moisten the salt until it sticks together like wet sand (you may add essential oils).

Warm your body in the shower or a bathtub. Turn the water off or stand up in the tub. Take about 1 tablespoon of moistened salt and rub it on your body. Cover the entire body starting with the arms, chest, and abdomen, using additional salt as needed. Rinse with cool water and towel dry.

Rest for 20 minutes to receive the full benefit.

Continue Your Exercise Program

Like with any lifestyle change, it may take a week or two to notice significant benefits or improvement in your depression. Remember, even antidepressant medications can take up to three weeks to cause a noticeable difference. Stay with your positive new exercise routine consistently and improvement will come.

Action Step 2.5 — Exercise

Are you exercising 45 minutes to 1 hour per day at least five days per week? ○ **yes**   ○ **no**

If yes, keep up the good work and don't let anything interrupt your new healthy habit.

If no, think about why you are not accomplishing this important goal. Almost any excuse you can raise has a solution if you are determined to get and stay well. Review the possible exercise choices in *Action Step 1.5* and select at least one you will do this week.

Write it here: _____

Tips for Success:

» Introduce a new sport or exercise into your routine.

» Warm up to avoid muscle strain.

» Listen to classical music as you exercise.

» Vary the exercise routine to increase caloric expenditure.

» If the climate makes it difficult to exercise outdoors, choose a shopping mall that encourages walkers or use an aerobic exercise video.

» Remember, there's no such thing as bad weather, only bad clothing!

» If disability is preventing exercise, talk with a trainer at a gym, YMCA, or community center that can develop an exercise routine to accommodate your limitations. Exercise is vital to your wellness.

» Conclude exercise with cooling down and stretching.

Interval Training (I.T.)

Interval training involves alternating a higher-intensity exercise (sprinting, speed-walking) with a lower-intensity exercise (walking), rather than continuous exertion at one level.

Imagine exercising very hard, relaxing a little, exercising just as hard again, and repeating the cycle for a set amount of time. If you are outside, you could run or speed walk a set distance (a tree, a mail box, etc.) then slow down to recover, repeating the sprint when you feel rested. Once you have finished exercising, it is a good idea to take 5 to 10 minutes to cool down. Do some gentle stretching and slow, comfortable walking to finish up. You can do I.T.

Action Step 2.6	Target Heart Rate (THR)
IC x (220 – age – RHR) + RHR = THR	$0.5* \times (220 - \underline{\hspace{1cm}} - \underline{\hspace{1cm}}) + \underline{\hspace{1cm}} = \underline{\hspace{1cm}}$ YOUR AGE RHR RHR THR
  (RHR) Resting Heart Rate **(IC)** Intensity Constant **(THR)** Target Heart Rate	Goal Heart Rate + 5 = Maximum Exercise Rate Goal Heart Rate – 5 = Minimum Heart Rate *Intermediate intensity constant *For more details refer to p. 31*

🗓 Organize Your Life

- » Plan and choose an exercise routine for the week. Mark it on a calendar or a planner.
- » Determine the proper gear (walking poles, pedometer, heart rate monitor, jumping rope, bike, etc.).
- » Obtain comfortable clothing and shoes.
- » Make provision for weather-appropriate items (sunscreen, cap, sunglasses, rain gear, etc.).
- » Look for a safe exercise place (walking trails, gym membership, park, etc.).
- » Map out your route and distance.
- » For accountability, consider an exercise companion.
- » Plan your breakfast the night before to give you more time to fit in a morning exercise. Keep in mind that exercise before breakfast is more beneficial for the brain.
- » Include your contrast shower or salt glow in your morning routine.

NUTRITION FOR THE BRAIN

3

DURING THIS SESSION YOU WILL LEARN:

How to enhance production of important neurotransmitters

A 4-step weight loss plan

The benefits of omega-3 for the brain

NUTRITION HITS

» Possibly the most overlooked cause of diminished mental power, depression, or anxiety

» Can have profound effects

» Once a _____ ✎ 3-a change is adopted, it takes 7 to 10 days to begin noticing a difference

» Gradual improvement continues

CLUES OF A "NUTRITION HIT"

» Dietary inventory indicates a lot of junk food and/or meat

» Signs of carbohydrate addiction

  › Sugar temporarily increases brain serotonin levels, helping the person "feel better"

» Low serum B_{12} or folate

» Often no obvious clues are present

NUTRITION HITS

» Insufficient dietary tryptophan

» Converted to serotonin, melatonin, and niacin (vitamin B_3)

» Tryptophan is the least abundant amino acid in the diet

» The conversion of tryptophan to 5-HTP is inhibited by stress, insulin resistance, magnesium or vitamin B_6 deficiency, lack of light, and increasing age

TRYPTOPHAN SUPPLEMENTATION IMPROVES

» Premenstrual dysphoria from ovulation (mid-cycle) to the 3rd day of menstruation

» Depression and seasonal affective disorder (SAD)

» Insomnia

» Obstructive sleep apnea

» Nicotine withdrawal

Foods Rich in Tryptophan (mg/100g)*

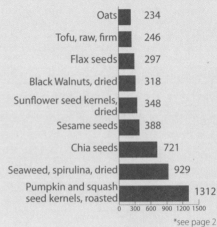

*see page 2

Ratio of Tryptophan to 5 Competing Amino Acids*

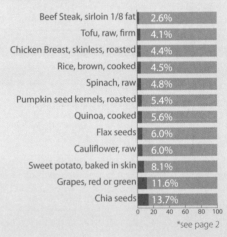

*see page 2

STRESS PRONE SUBJECTS AND NUTRITION[1]

» In stress-prone subjects, _____ ✎3-b carbohydrate, _____ ✎3-c protein food prevents a deterioration of mood and performance under uncontrollable laboratory stress conditions

» Stress-prone subjects have a higher risk of brain serotonin deficiency

» In such subjects, higher natural carbohydrates increase personal control

» Carbohydrates prevent a functional shortage of central serotonin during acute stress, due to their potentiating effect on brain tryptophan

TYROSINE SUPPLEMENTATION IN RESPONSE TO STRESS[2, 3]

» Those given tyrosine had significantly reduced headache, stress, fatigue, muscle aches, and sleepiness compared to controls

» Improvements were noted in mood and mental states (happiness, mental clarity, hostility, and tension) and cognitive tests (math skills, coding map compass, and pattern recognition) in the tyrosine group

» Feelings of vigor and improvements in blood pressure

THE IRONIC CONCLUSION

» Don't chow down on high protein sources to boost either tyrosine or tryptophan

» Emphasize carbohydrate-rich plant sources of nutrition

Tyrosine (mg/100g)

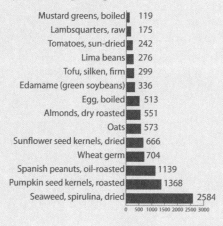

Mustard greens, boiled	119
Lambsquarters, raw	175
Tomatoes, sun-dried	242
Lima beans	276
Tofu, silken, firm	299
Edamame (green soybeans)	336
Egg, boiled	513
Almonds, dry roasted	551
Oats	573
Sunflower seed kernels, dried	666
Wheat germ	704
Spanish peanuts, oil-roasted	1139
Pumpkin seed kernels, roasted	1368
Seaweed, spirulina, dried	2584

Ratio of Tyrosine to 3 Competing Amino Acids

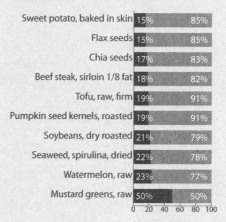

Sweet potato, baked in skin	15%	85%
Flax seeds	15%	85%
Chia seeds	17%	83%
Beef steak, sirloin 1/8 fat	18%	82%
Tofu, raw, firm	19%	91%
Pumpkin seed kernels, roasted	19%	91%
Soybeans, dry roasted	21%	79%
Seaweed, spirulina, dried	22%	78%
Watermelon, raw	23%	77%
Mustard greens, raw	50%	50%

Dietary Sources Of Folate*

FOOD ITEM	SERVING	FOLATE (mcg)
Black-eyed peas, cooked	1 cup/172g	358
Lentils, cooked	1 cup/198g	358
Pinto beans, cooked	1 cup/171g	294
Black beans, cooked	1 cup/172g	256
Asparagus, boiled	1 cup/180g	243
Mustard greens, raw	1 cup/56g	105
Spinach, raw	1 cup/30g	58

*see page 2

NUTRITIONAL CAUSES OF DEPRESSION[4, 5, 6, 7, 8]

» Insufficient dietary tryptophan

» Insufficient dietary tyrosine

» Low folate levels (such depression unresponsive to medication)

» Low folate levels (such depression unresponsive to medication)

» Atherosclerosis causing heart disease or mini strokes

HIGH CHOLESTEROL AND THE BRAIN[9]

» Patients with major depression tend to have significantly higher _____ ✎ 3-d levels than healthy adults

» Depressed patients with elevated cholesterol have a poorer prognosis for treatment response.

» Lowering cholesterol improves depression and mood, and improves (decreases) impulsivity

FOODS CONTAINING HARMFUL CHOLESTEROL BYPRODUCTS

Sources of the most harmful cholesterol to monkey aortas are:

1. Custard mixes

2. Pancake mixes

3. Lard and Parmesan cheese

Cholesterol in Foods

FOOD ITEM (3 OZ.)	CHOLESTEROL. (mg)
Fruits	0
Grains	0
Nuts	0
Vegetables	0
Milk, non-fat 1c	4
Milk, 2%, 1c	18
Milk, whole, 1c	33
Egg white	0
Mayonnaise	8
Ice cream, 1/2c	29
Butter, 1 Tbs	31
Egg, 1 large	213
Tuna	26
Clams	57
Crab	64
Chicken breast, no skin	73
Pork	76
Chicken breast & skin	80
Oyster	82
Shrimp	165
Beef kidney	329
Beef liver	410
Caviar	500
Beef brains	1697

Changes in Psychological Distress in the Lifestyle Heart Trial

Anxiety, depression, insomnia, & anhedonia (inability to experience pleasure) index

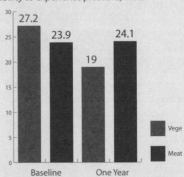

IRON AND MENTAL PERFORMANCE[10]

» Iron deficiency anemia is common, particularly in women, and is associated with apathy, depression, and rapid fatigue when exercising

» Essential for good athletic performance, scholastic performance, and cognitive function

» Iron-dependent neurotransmitters include:

› Dopamine

› Serotonin

› Norepinephrine

› GABA

THIAMINE (VITAMIN B$_1$)[11]

In four double-blind studies, an improvement in thiamine status was associated with improved mood.

CHOLINE AND BETAINE[12]

» Betaine lowers homocysteine levels

» Choline improves memory and focus

» Important for developing and protecting the brain in utero (must get from the mother)

» Choline is critical to manufacture acetylcholine

RESVERATROL

» May improve the blood flow to the brain by up to 30%

» May help protect the brain from dementia

» Grape skin extract, which is high in resveratrol, protects against the toxicity of beta amyloid protein and also against free radical damage

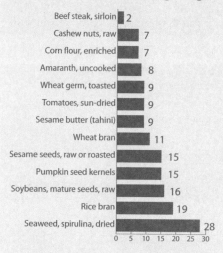

Iron Content Of Foods (mg/100g)

Food	Iron (mg/100g)
Beef steak, sirloin	2
Cashew nuts, raw	7
Corn flour, enriched	7
Amaranth, uncooked	8
Wheat germ, toasted	9
Tomatoes, sun-dried	9
Sesame butter (tahini)	9
Wheat bran	11
Sesame seeds, raw or roasted	15
Pumpkin seed kernels	15
Soybeans, mature seeds, raw	16
Rice bran	19
Seaweed, spirulina, dried	28

Thiamine Content of Select Foods

FOOD ITEM	SERVING	THIAMINE (mcg)
Rice bran	1 cup/118g	3.2
Wheat germ	1 cup/115g	2.2
Macadamia nuts	1 cup/134g	1.6
Flaxseed	½ cup/84g	2.8
Oats	1 cup/156g	1.2
Oat bran, raw	1 cup/94g	1.1
Pistachio nuts, dry roasted	1 cup/123g	1.0
Sunflower seed kernels, dry	1 cup/46g	0.7

Choline Content (mg/100g)

FOOD ITEM	CHOLINE	BETAINE	SUM OF BOTH
Quinoa, uncooked	70	630	700
Spinach, raw	18	550	568
Lambsquarters, raw	20	332	352
Soy flour	192	3	195
Beets, raw	6	129	135
Soybeans, raw	116	2	118
Whole grain wheat	31	73	104
Barley flour or meal	38	66	104
Flaxseed	79	3	82

NUTRITION FOR THE BRAIN, part 2

NUTRITIONAL ISSUES AND LACK OF MENTAL POWER

» Insufficient dietary tryptophan

» Insufficient dietary tyrosine

» Excess cholesterol

» Insufficient dietary folate

» Insufficient iron

» Insufficient thiamine, choline, resveratrol

» Low omega-3 fatty acid intake

OMEGA-3 BRAIN BENEFITS IN HEALTHY PERSONS[13, 14]

» Improved frontal lobe function

» Improved sense of wellbeing

» Increased vigor and energy

» Improved reaction time

» Improved attention

» Improved test scores

» Improved mood

» Better control of thoughts and behavior and less impulsivity

» Decreases risk of at-risk young people becoming psychotic

» Helps prevent major depression/anxiety in women with psychological distress

» Decreases anger in men with aggressive behaviors and problems with the law

» Clinical response of over 50% in those with major depression and/or anxiety

Non-Wine Resveratrol Sources

FOOD ITEM (3 oz)	RESVERATROL (Ng/g dry sample)
Red grapes (Merlot)	6356
Ligonberries	5884
Red grapes (Pinot Noir)	5746
Peanuts (boiled)	5100
Blueberries	1691
Cranberries	900
Bilberries	768

Arachidonic acid (present in meat and eggs) in the diet also can decrease mental power.

» Improves bipolar disorder

» Improves memory in those with _____ ✎ 3-e
related cognitive decline

» Improves aggression and depression in those with
borderline personality disorder

» Lowers risk of dementia

» Can improve some aspects of ADHD

» Improves IQ in babies of mothers who breast feed and get
adequate amounts in their diet

E.P.A RECOMMENDATIONS FOR YOUNG CHILDREN, PREGNANT AND NURSING WOMEN AND WOMEN WHO COULD GET PREGNANT (ADAPTED)[15]

» Avoid all consumption of mercury-rich fish like shark,
swordfish, king mackerel, and tilefish

» Limit fish consumption to one average sized meal per
week if you are eating local fish where no safety advisories
are available. (If there are local warnings—heed those
admonitions.)

» Even when fish are lower in mercury, limit intake to
two average-sized meals per week. (The Environmental
Protection Agency states that "nearly all fish and shellfish
contain traces of mercury.")

MERCURY AND FISH

The connection between eating fish and body mercury
levels is so strong that researchers seeking to determine
_____ ✎ 3-f exposures among groups of
people often look at only one dietary factor: fish consumption.

Omega-3 fats are an essential part of the diet (we cannot manufacture them from other nutrients).

Biomagnification Of DDD Insecticide

SAMPLE SITE	DDD, PPM
Lake water	0.02
Phytoplankton (living in DDD-contaminated water)	5
Herbivorous fish (they eat the phytoplankton)	40-300
Carnivorous fish (they eat the herbivorous fish)	Up to 2500

How Most People Get Omega-3

FISH	AMOUNT	OMEGA-3 (mg)
Drum fish	1	810
Tuna (in water)	1 serv.	930
Rainbow trout	1	1180
Freshwater bass	3.5 oz	1190
Pink salmon	3.5 oz	1710
Herring	3.5 oz	3000
Halibut	3.5 oz	3160
Shad fillet	1 cup	3680
Atlantic mackerel	3.5 oz	3930

MERCURY TOXICITY AND THE BRAIN

» Insomnia

» Nervousness

» Hallucinations

» Memory loss

» Headache

» Dizziness

» Anxiety

» Irritability

» Daytime drowsiness

» Emotional instability

» Depression

» Poor cognitive function

OTHER TOXINS THAT IMPAIR MENTAL PERFORMANCE

» Polychlorinated biphenyls (PCBs)

» Dioxins

» Pesticides:

› DDT

› Heptachlor

› Dieldrin

» Lead

» Polychlorinated napthalenes (PCNs)

THREE DIFFERENT TYPES OF OMEGA-3[16]

» ALA

› Present in land plant sources

» EPA

› Largest omega-3 in most fish but also present in water plants

» DHA

› Also present in water plants and fish

» ALA turns into EPA which can turn into DHA

› Requires vitamin B_3, vitamin B_6, Magnesium, Zinc, and vitamin C

Sources of Mercury:

» fish

» vapor from amalgam fillings

» burning coal

» animals that eat fish

» volcanos

» forest fires

» manufacture of metals, alkali

PLANT-BASED DIETS AND DHA[17]

» Lifelong plant based vegetarians still have DHA in their brain

» Their rates of conversion of ALA into EPA and then DHA in preliminary research seems to be better

» They can still eat water-plant sources or water plant DHA supplements

» Water-plant DHA supplements are the only type of supplemental DHA that has been shown to improve learning and memory

OBESITY ASSOCIATED WITH DEPRESSION

» Obesity associated with low energy levels

» After meal blood sugars in excess of 140 mg/dl associated with fatigue

» Getting on a weight loss program and losing more than 5 pounds can bring about improved energy levels and mood.

FOUR STEP WEIGHT LOSS PLAN

1. No snacks. Drink only water between meals.

2. Eat a good breakfast and a moderate lunch. Eliminate the evening meal. If something "must" be eaten in the evening, whole fruit is all that is allowable.

3. Eliminate or at least greatly reduce refined sugar and free fats or fatty foods in the diet, while emphasizing foods high in fiber.

4. Daily moderate exercise for at least 45 minutes a day.

Plant-Based Omega-3 Sources*

FOOD ITEM	SERVING	OMEGA-3 (mg)
Flaxseed, ground	1 oz/28g	6388
Chia seeds, dried	1 oz/28g	4915
Walnuts, English	1 oz/28g	2524
Hemp seed	1 oz/28g	2000
Wheat germ oil	1 Tbs/14g	932
Green soybeans	1 cup/155g	569
Pecans	1 oz/28g	276
Avocado	1 whole/136g	221
Sweet red pepper	1 oz/28g	217
Blueberries, fresh	1 cup/148g	86

*see page 2

ALA
alha-linelolic acid

EPA
eicosapentaenoic acid

DHA
docosahexaenoic acid

Long chain omega-3

MENTAL HEALTH ADVANTAGES TO EATING A BALANCED BREAKFAST[18, 19]

» Better cognitive performance

» Better scholastic scores (improved learning and memory)

» Improved creativity

» Link between skipping _____ ✎3-g and depression in 5000 university students

» Breakfast eaters have a more positive mood, performed better on spatial orientation tests and felt calmer at the end of the testing

FOLATE AND VITAMIN B_{12} DEFICIENCY[20]

» The common mediator of the effects of B_{12} and folate deficiency may be reduced SAMe

» Correction of folate and vitamin B_{12} deficiencies may alleviate depressive symptoms and augment the response to antidepressant therapy, perhaps because of the resultant increase in SAMe concentrations

DIDEROT'S PROVERB

"Doctors are always working to preserve our health and cooks to destroy it. But the latter are often the more successful."

Hydroxycobalamin is the preferred B_{12} supplement since it is also detoxifying.

⚙ What You Learned

» Lowering cholesterol levels improve depression and impulsivity

» How to produce more brain EPA and DHA

» Correction of folic acid and vitamin B_{12} deficiencies may alleviate depressive symptoms

Reading Prescription

» *Depression: the Way Out,* chapter 4

» Chapter in the book of Proverbs that corresponds with each day's date

» *SOS Help for Emotions: Managing Anxiety, Anger and Depression,* chapters 7, 8, and 9

» *Telling Yourself the Truth,* chapters 4 and 5

LIFESTYLE IN ACTION

Brain Neurotransmitters

Serotonin

Signs of a brain serotonin deficit are feeling anxious, shaky, trembling, and on edge. A lack of serotonin can also cause an inability to stay calm, sleeplessness, or intermittent feelings of panic or impending doom. Frustration tolerance tends to go down, meaning that mild to moderate stressors are not handled well. Feelings of deep sadness with crying spells, or feelings of emptiness can often be the result of inadequate serotonin. Additional manifestations along with other errors of thought can lead to obsessive compulsive disorder, or social phobias. With symptoms or manifestations such as these, it is imperative that the individual do what is necessary to improve serotonin levels naturally. Medications that manipulate serotonin receptors may produce selective and limited improvement in some of these symptoms but with a frequent worsening of impulsivity and an "I don't care attitude" even in things we should care about enough to try and change. Even with these benefits, half of the people will quit taking the medications due to bothersome physical side effects. Therefore, if you have any of these symptoms, boosting serotonin naturally can be life changing. This requires not only tryptophan, the precursor of serotonin, but enough carbs to get the tryptophan into the brain. In addition, higher amounts of magnesium and vitamin B_6, bright light, and physical exercise can help. If these measures do not produce a significant response within 2 weeks, a 5-HTP supplement may help. If sleeplessness is a symptom, taking the 5-HTP near bedtime may help.

Norepinephrine

Signs of brain norepinephrine deficiency include lack of concentration, problems with fatigue, possible daytime sleepiness or desiring to sleep all the time, irritability, brain fog, loss of memory, and struggling with classes or activities that require thinking or pattern recognition. When norepinephrine levels improve, patients are consistent in reporting increased happiness, energy, and clarity of thinking. Boosting norepinephrine not only requires foods high in tyrosine, but foods that are lower in protein and higher in natural carbohydrates. In addition, sufficient folate (vitamin B_9) and vitamin B_{12} is necessary to make adequate amounts. This is why people low in B_{12} may notice a tremendous energy boost after a B_{12} shot. Good sources of vitamin B_{12} include, Red Star brand nutritional yeast, fortified breakfast cereals, fortified plant based milks, and B_{12} (hydroxycobalamin) supplements.

Dopamine

Signs of a dopamine deficiency includes apathy, a decrease in ability to experience pleasure, and lack of motivation. People with a rather severe dopamine deficit often withdraw from society and activities as much as possible. Sometimes when family members try to get them to go out and eat with them at a restaurant, if they go, while everyone is eating and socializing, the only thing that person with a dopamine deficit is thinking is how they can't wait to leave and go back home. Lack of dopamine can adversely affect social relations. In some cases it can lead to diminished libido and lack of appetite (leading to anorexia).

In addition it can also negatively affect desire for love and friendship. One of the more common symptoms of a lack of dopamine or dopamine receptors is a loss of desire for learning new things. Many school dropouts occur simply due to a dopamine deficit. Dopamine increases motivation. It also causes us to want, desire, seek out, and search. We must have enough tyrosine, folate, and vitamin B_{12} in the brain to make dopamine. Plant based sources that are lower in protein and higher in natural carbohydrates eaten in their whole plant sources, eaten whole (not juiced or refined) help a great deal.

Unhealthy food (rich foods, sugary sweets and chocolates) and unhealthy sexual practices will decrease dopamine receptors and dopamine levels. This can result in being more sensitive and more irritable with the usual nuisances of life. Anxiety then goes up. Reduced impulse control results with a weakened ability to foresee consequences, and a weakened willpower. This is why some people with a dopamine deficit struggle with food and/or sex addictions and why some people gain weight and become obese. Restoring both dopamine and dopamine receptors sometimes requires a 90 day reboot where the person is totally abstinent from addictive foods and/or sex to restore both the dopamine levels and the dopamine receptors.

Often people with depression or anxiety are lacking in more than one of these important neurotransmitters, and some are lacking in all three.

No Cholesterol and Arachidonic Acid

Avoiding these in the food supply promotes optimal brain health. Start by eliminating meat, cheese, eggs, and milk. If you can't do it all at once, start by eliminating meat first, then cheese, then, eggs, and finally milk, while replacing these foods with healthy foods recommended in this section. Lowering your saturated fat intake will also help you to lower your blood cholesterol significantly. (Lard, butter, coconut, and palm oils). Experiment with veggie based casseroles and stir fry dishes.

Brain Essentials

Tryptophan: pumpkin, sesame and sunflower seeds, tofu, cauliflower, walnuts, flaxseed, and grapes.

Tyrosine: watermelon, almonds, lentils, whole grains (wheat and oats), bananas, lima beans, avocados, seaweed (spirulina), and dry roasted soy beans.

No Cholesterol: whole grains, fruits, vegetables, and nuts.

Iron: seaweed, soy beans, pumpkin and sesame seeds, cashews, raisins, and sun dried tomatoes.

Thiamine: macadamia nuts, pistachios, fresh green peas, edamame, navy beans, and asparagus.

Choline and Betaine: quinoa, spinach, green soybeans, and beets.

Resveratrol: bilberries, blueberries, black grapes, peanuts, and cranberries.

Omega-3: walnuts, pecans, red bell pepper, avocado, blueberries, romaine lettuce, spinach, flax, chia, and hemp seeds.

Folate: black eyed peas, pinto beans, black beans, chick peas, asparagus, and spinach.

B_{12}: Red Star brand nutritional yeast, fortified breakfast cereals and plant based milks.

Action Step 3.1   Make a Salad

Make a fruit or vegetable salad using the ingredients listed above.

Tryptophan _____

Tyrosine _____

Iron _____

Omega-3 _____

Thiamine _____

Choline and Betaine _____

Resveratrol _____

Folate _____

B_{12} _____

What to Eat

The average American eats only 6 entrées a month. Of course they eat each of the six dishes multiple times per month. Keep experimenting until you can find six very healthy and very tasty main entrées that you especially enjoy. Then alternate these and you will have the same variety in your diet as the typical American, but with far better mental and physical results. Then you can continue to build on these six every month. As you do this you will actually have MORE variety with even better taste than what you used to eat.

Action Step 3.2	Healthy Meal Planning

List at least three new healthy dishes you plan to make this week:

_____

_____

_____

_____

_____

Note: *for recipe ideas, turn to Appendix X in Depression: the Way Out.*

Tips For Eating Smart When Eating Out

With more and more people eating out, there may be a concern of maintaining a depression free lifestyle and still enjoy a variety of options. Look for restaurants that offer healthy menu choices.

When ordering, study the menu for vegan/vegetarian dishes. If none are available, here are some suggestions:

» Talk to the restaurant manager about special options

» Order the side dishes without the meat to make a full veggie plate

» Use a baked potato with veggies as topping instead of mashed potato and gravy or French fries

» By request, sandwiches can be made with avocado, grilled veggies, portabella mushroom

» For pizza option request extra sauce and vegetables with no cheese

» Replace cheese and sour cream with extra vegetables

» Inquire about animal fat in beans, soups, and rice

» Look for foods that are steamed, roasted, baked or grilled

Continue Your Exercise Program

Are you keeping with your exercise program? Is it becoming a routine in your daily schedule just like eating, bathing, sleeping?

Action Step 3.3 — Exercise

1. What exercise did you do last week?

_____

2. What time of the day works best to routinely exercise?

_____

3. What type of exercise do you plan on doing this week?

_____

4. At least once this week include your family or close friend in your exercise plan. What can you do together (walking, gardening, frisbee, playing catch, hiking, tennis)?

_____

📅 Organize Your Life

Being able to maintain a fast pace in the kitchen will make cooking a pleasant activity. Here are some suggestions to keep an organized kitchen and minimize the cleaning time required after cooking/serving. (Many people like to cook, but don't enjoy the cleaning involved with the process!)

Kitchen tips:

» Reuse a pot (rinse if needed) instead of reaching for another clean one.

» Empty the dishwasher as soon as the cycle is complete. Then it is immediately available to use. Place the dirty dishes in the dishwasher as soon as you finish using them. This can be every family member's job, including young children. When cleaning the table after a large dinner, stack the dirty dishes; gather utensils, and pile leftovers together to avoid multiple trips to the sink.

» Have soapy water in the sink, and as you cook wash the dishes immediately.

» Gather all needed ingredients to cook a recipe all at once, and return them to the proper place as soon as they are used.

» As you open cans, food packages, and jars, dispose lids, wrappers, jars in the proper bins or trash immediately.

» When peeling vegetables and fruit, do it over a paper towel or a bag. When you are finished with peeling or coring, fold the paper containing the unwanted remains and compost or throw in the trash.

» De-clutter. Make as much counter space available as possible. Put away kitchen appliances that are not frequently used.

» Clean the refrigerator weekly, discarding the "forgotten" leftovers.

» Organize and restock your pantry with new recommended healthier food items.

» Keep a small vase for fresh cut flowers (wild flowers and the ones from your yard are extra special!) or a small potted plant by your kitchen window. This is one way to stop and smell the roses!

HOW THINKING CAN DEFEAT DEPRESSION OR ANXIETY

4

DURING THIS SESSION YOU WILL LEARN:

The benefits of Cognitive Behavior Therapy (CBT)

The five components of Emotional Intelligence (EQ)

How to implement Cognitive Behavior Therapy (CBT)

EFFECTS OF COGNITIVE THERAPY LAST LONGER[1]

» 240 patients with moderate to severe depression were randomized to receive medications or cognitive behavior therapy

» 57% of both groups responded positively

» Of the responders, at one year, 75% of the _____ 4-a therapy group remained free of relapse

» Among those taking an antidepressant, 60% who remained on medication were relapse-free compared with just 19% of those who were switched to a placebo

WHAT IS COGNITIVE BEHAVIOR THERAPY?

» A cognition is a thought or perception

» Your cognitions are the way you are thinking about things at any moment, including this very moment

» These thoughts have a significant impact on how you feel, which in turn has a significant impact on how you "behave"

EMOTIONAL INTELLIGENCE

» Contributes more to successful and enjoyable living than I.Q.

» Since emotional intelligence is learned, rather than inherited, it can be improved

5 COMPONENTS OF E.Q.

1. Knowing our emotions
2. Managing our emotions
3. Recognizing emotions in others
4. Managing relationships with others
5. Motivating ourselves to achieve our _____ 4-b

In the first three chapters, we learned how our physical behaviors can affect our thoughts and emotions. This section shows how our thoughts influence/drive our emotions and behavior.

CBT EFFECTIVELY TREATS

» Depression

» Phobias

» Obsessive-compulsive disorder

» Post-traumatic stress disorder

» Panic

» Anxiety

» Anorexia

» Bulimia

» Addictions such as alcoholism

BENEFITS OF CBT

» Is at least as effective as drug therapy

» Has no physical side-effects

» Makes relapse less likely

» Makes staying free from mental illness more likely

» Changes brain chemistry

FEELINGS AND THOUGHTS

» Your _____ 🔑 4-c result from the messages you give yourself

» Your thoughts have much more to do with how you feel than what is actually happening in your life

UNFULFILLED?

» You are not smart enough, successful enough, attractive enough, or talented enough to feel happy and fulfilled

» Or your negative feelings are strictly due to others

» Bad things do happen and life beats up on most of us at times

It's great news that our thoughts determine our emotions and behavior because this section teaches how you can change your thoughts and significantly change your emotions and behavior.

What we think affects who we are.

_____

_____

_____

_____

_____

_____

_____

_____

_____

WHY UNFULFILLED

» All of these thoughts have the tendency to make us victims–because we think the causes result from something beyond our control

» In contrast, you can change: the way you think about things and you can also change your basic _____ ⚲ 4-d and _____. ⚲ 4-e When you do, you will often experience lasting changes in your mood, outlook, and productivity.

RESEARCH[2, 3]

» Research has documented that negative thoughts which cause emotional turmoil nearly always contain gross distortions

» The thoughts on the surface appear valid, but you will learn that they are irrational or just plain wrong and that twisted thinking is a major cause of suffering

CROOKED THINKING

» Also called A—C Thinking

» Believing that we have little or no ability to influence our _____ ⚲ 4-f and that events and situations directly cause our emotions and behavior

IDENTIFY CROOKED A—C THINKING[4]

1. "She hurt my feelings by what she said."

2. "My boss really made me mad, and the more I thought about what he did, the madder I got."

3. "I got _____ ⚲ 4-g all upset over that clerk's behavior."

CBT helps to develop integrity. Integrity goes beyond truthfulness. It's also taking responsibility for how one feels and what one does.

> **The A-B-C of CBT**
> A–ACTIVATING EVENT
> B–BELIEF
> C–EMOTIONAL CONSEQUENCE

_____
_____
_____
_____
_____
_____
_____
_____
_____
_____

1. ALL–OR–NOTHING THINKING

» "It's completely ruined."

» "She is perfect."

RESULTS OF ALL–OR–NOTHING THINKING

› Low self-worth

› Procrastination

› Interferes with goals

› Inflation of a problem

› Frustration

› Pessimism

› Discouragement

› Suicidal thoughts

CORRECTING ALL–OR–NOTHING THOUGHTS

› "I'm a total failure!" replaced with "I am reasonably good at some things."

› "I'm too out of shape for this exercise program, guess I'll give up!" replaced with "I can work up to this exercise routine, and just trying will have a _____ ⚲ 4-h impact."

2. OVERGENERALIZATION

» Unintentionally exaggerating

» "How come the kids always obey me, but never listen to you?"

» "You are always late!"

» Watch out for the words "Always" and "Never"

The Lost Art of Thinking by Neil Nedley, M.D. is a supplemental book that can greatly assist you in understanding the ten ways of distorted thinking and how to correct these thoughts.

3. MENTAL FILTER

» Having blinders on

THERE IS NOTHING GOOD IN MY LIFE[4]

› Job stinks, wife nags
› Leaky Roof, bills
› Boss yelling at me
› I'm short and fat
› I'm going bald

GOOD THINGS IN LIFE

› Enjoy the children
› Close friends
› Wife is very attractive
› Sleeps well
› Can feed myself
› Have no difficulty breathing
› Can walk well
› Enjoy my church
› Have the potential to do a lot of things

OVERCOMING MENTAL FILTER

Intentionally, forcefully look for evidence that supports a different way of thinking.

It's not what we don't know that hurts us so much, it's what we know for sure that just ain't so.

—WILL ROGERS

Overgeneralization
Holding the hypothesis as a fact rather than a hypothesis.

Our imagination was not given us to be allowed to run riot and have its own way, without any effort at restraint and discipline.

—ELLEN WHITE

HOW THINKING CAN DEFEAT DEPRESSION OR ANXIETY, part 2

4. MIND READING[5]

» "John has been through treatment so many times. I know he will never quit drinking, so why even bring it up?"

» Don't judge motives

» You can judge actions

» Only 1 in 4 chance you'll be right with strangers or those you don't know well

» Women and men are equal in their ability to read the minds of others.

» Up to 4 out of 5 _____ 4-i that you'll be right in those you are very close to.

5. FORTUNE TELLER ERROR

» "I will never be able to overcome this problem."

» Watch out for self-fulfilling prophecies

» Panic disorder

» "I must worry about this, otherwise it might happen."

» "What is the worst thing that could happen?"

» "What if it did happen?"

» "Is it likely to be as dreadful as it appears to me now?"

> **If the thoughts are wrong, the feelings will be wrong; and the thoughts and feelings combined make up the moral character.**
>
> —ELLEN WHITE

6. MAGNIFICATION OR MINIMIZATION

» Majoring in minors and minoring in majors

» "These new laws affecting my business are terrible!"

» "Is not this great Babylon which I have built?"

—DANIEL 4:30

» The five foolish virgins minimized the importance of having adequate oil in their lamps. By the time they came to their senses and realized their need, it was too late.

—MATTHEW 25

» "I can't stand it!"

» "When trials arise that seem unexplainable, we should not allow our peace to be spoiled. However unjustly we may be treated, let not passion arise. By indulging a spirit of retaliation we injure ourselves."

—CHRIST OBJECT LESSONS 172

7. EMOTIONAL REASONING

» "I feel angry at you, proving that you have been cruel and insensitive to me."

» "I don't feel like _____ ✎ 4-j anything right now, and so I won't."

8. MISLABELING

» "A person is lazy if she doesn't wash the dishes after she eats."

» "If a woman cares about me, she will do this for me every day."

» "If a man doesn't spend all his time with me he is selfish."

...for man looketh on the outward appearance, but the Lord looketh on the heart.

—1 SAMUEL 16:7

Take Your H.A.T. Off
Horrible, **A**wful, **T**errible

♪

I don't like it. I don't like it.
It's ok. It's ok.
I can stand it anyway.
I can stand it anyway.
I'm alright. I'm alright.

(to the tune of *Frère Jacques*)

_____

_____

_____

_____

9. PERSONALIZATION

» "I can't believe they did that to me!"

» In many cases, the person didn't even know you were upset by what they did, much less did it intentionally to hurt you

» "The boss gave that lesson just for me."

» Haman took the refusal of Mordecai so personally that he was willing to wipe out the entire Jewish nation to get revenge on one man

—BOOK OF ESTHER

10. DISQUALIFYING THE POSITIVE

» You feel so bad about yourself that you think compliments directed your way are given out of pity—and thus _____ 🔑 4-k

» The distortion that most adversely affects motivation or personal achievement

» "Obstacles are those frightful things you see when you take your eyes off your goal."

—HANNAH MORE

» "Think you can, think you can't. Either way you'll be right."

—HENRY FORD

» "I don't think of all the misery but of the beauty that still remains."

—ANNE FRANK

» "Determine that the thing can and shall be done, and then we shall find the way."

—ABRAHAM LINCOLN

Nothing gives one person so much advantage over another as to remain cool and unruffled under all circumstances.

— THOMAS JEFFERSON

Each one is tempted when he is dragged away and enticed by his own evil feelings.

—JAMES 1:14

Feelings are much like waves. We can't stop them from coming, but we can choose which one to surf.

—JONATAN MÅRTENSSON

TRUTH IN THE HEART

"LORD, who may abide in Your tabernacle?
Who may dwell in Your holy hill?
He who walks uprightly, And works righteousness,
And speaks the truth in his heart."

—PSALM 15:1-2

CBT IS NOT NEW

"Whatever is true, whatever is honest, whatever is just,... if there be any virtue, and if there be any praise, think on these things."

—PHILIPPIANS 4:8

MISBELIEF BREAKERS

- » On what facts do I base this notion?
- » What are the most effective arguments I can come up with to contest this notion?
- » Could the facts in this situation be explained in other ways?
- » Are there alternative interpretations that I could give that would be more truthful and less painful. If so, what are they?

FINDING THE EVIDENCE

- » What is the evidence that this thought is true or false?
- » If my best friend said this, what would I say to him/her?
- » When I'm not feeling this way, would I think this?
- » What do ultimate sources of truth say?

And be not conformed to this world: but be ye transformed by the renewing of your mind...

—ROMANS 12:2

Feeling Better vs. Getting Better

The first can occur spontaneously.

The second results from applying and reapplying the methods of accurate thinking.

Truth will ultimately prevail where there is pains taken to bring it to light.

—GEORGE WASHINGTON

STEPS TO USING CBT

1. Listen to and analyze your thoughts
2. Look for possible distortions in your thoughts and label those distortions
3. Reconstruct your thinking
4. PRACTICE, PRACTICE, PRACTICE

» Realistic thinking does not come naturally

» It must be a conscious choice followed by strong effort

» The more balanced feelings that result will be worth the struggle and the effort

LET THIS MIND BE IN YOU

» A = Activating event

» B = Belief—Irrational belief replaced with true belief

» C = Consequence—Sorrow often turned into joy

» D = Dispute—Faulty beliefs uprooted

» E = Evaluate—Disappointment-really an appointment!

» F = Future—Believing, Bold, Blessed

» G = Goal—First your own circle, then the community, then the nation, then the world

For as he thinks in his heart, so is he.

—PROVERBS 23:7

You shall know the truth, and the truth shall make you free.

—JOHN 8:32

Scripture is an interesting and thought provoking source of truth and right thinking.

What You Learned

» Cognitive Behavior Therapy is just as effective, if not more, than taking drug medications to solve mental health problems

» Analyzing your thoughts to find your misbeliefs and cognitive distortions can help you restructure your thinking

» Change takes practice, but the benefits are more than worth the struggle and effort once you see the progress you have made

Reading Prescription

» *Depression: the Way Out,* chapter 10

» Chapter in the book of Proverbs that corresponds with each day's date

» *SOS Help for Emotions: Managing Anxiety, Anger and Depression, chapters* 10 and 11

» *Telling Yourself the Truth:* chapters 6, 7, and 8

LIFESTYLE IN ACTION

Accentuate the Positive, Eliminate the Negative

Our thoughts and our behaviors are related. ("For as the thoughts of his heart are, so is he." —Proverbs 23:7) You may have learned many new things in this session. Practicing these CBT exercises should help you manage your negative thoughts. This in turn will help you not speak harsh, critical words.

Action Step 4.1   Avoid Critical Speaking

Have you successfully gone two weeks without speaking any critical, negative comments? (We started this exercise in Session 1) ○ **yes** ○ **no**

If you have, **congratulations!** No doubt, you have noticed a change in your thought pattern. Maintaining this healthy new habit can really benefit you.

If your answer was no, **don't give up**. You are probably much more aware now, when you get ready to utter those negative statements, than you were before. Each day you attempt this exercise, your mind is being trained into a new pattern of thought. When you catch yourself saying something critical and have to start over your 14 day count, start that hour. Don't be tempted to let the rest of the day go being just as critical as you used to be.

*Note: pay close attention to the "constructive criticism" you now use so it does not slip into "destructive criticism." **Example:** "You are always late!" (destructive)*
        "Our office runs smooth when you are here on time." (constructive)

Four Steps of Cognitive Behavioral Therapy

Use these four important steps of CBT to identify and correct thinking errors and negative automatic thoughts.

1. **Hear** your internal dialogue
   What are you thinking?

2. **Analyze** your internal dialogue
   Identify which cognitive distortions are present.

3. **Reconstruct** your thinking
   Write true statements to replace distorted thoughts.

4. **Practice**, practice, practice
   The more you practice the easier it gets to eliminate distorted thinking.

Action Step 4.2 — Cognitive Distortions

Please match the definition with the corresponding cognitive distortion.

8 All-or-Nothing Thinking

5 Overgeneralization

6 Mental Filter

9 Mind Reading

2 Fortune Teller Error

1 Magnification or Minimization

10 Personalization

7 Emotional Reasoning

4 Labeling and Mislabeling

3 Disqualifying the Positive

1. Majoring in minors and minoring in majors.

2. Knowing that if THIS happens, THAT will definitely occur.

3. Acknowledging the good, appearing to be objective, but believing the good side has no value.

4. Habitually defining ourselves or others with a descriptive term.

5. Using limited factual evidence to hold a firm belief that actually is not true.

6. Singling out one aspect of a situation to the complete exclusion of others that should be considered.

7. Your feelings don't lie.

8. There is no "in between." It's completely one way or the other.

9. Having the certainty of knowing what another person is thinking without having to ask.

10. You are totally responsible for the good or bad that happens to you.

Action Step 4.3 — Identify and Correct Thinking Errors

Using the list of distortions, identify and correct thinking errors, wrong interpretations of events, and negative automatic thoughts that occur this week. Remember the four steps of Cognitive Behavior Therapy (p. 79).

The ABCs of CBT (Activating event, Beliefs, Consequences.)

Example: You passed a friend on a busy street. You thought they saw you but they didn't acknowledge you when you waved hello. You concluded that they were mad at you. Probably this is not true but it hurt your feelings just the same. The belief might be: "Sally didn't return my greeting and is mad at me or doesn't like me anymore. I feel worthless and unlovable." The distortion involved could be "Mind Reading" which is a "Jumping to Conclusions" error. A possible reconstruction could be: "Sally might have had something else on her mind and didn't even notice my wave. But even if she had seen me and ignored me, I am still a worthwhile person who has positive qualities to bring to a friendship."

Step 1: Think about a time where you experienced a strong negative emotion. It may have been anger, loneliness, sadness, rejection, or frustration. While recalling what you thought and felt at the time, write down your beliefs and thoughts on a separate sheet of paper. Do not worry about critiquing them at this time; just record what you remember.

_____

_____

Step 2: Now look at the list of thoughts and beliefs you have recorded. Do you see any distortions in your thinking? If someone you knew were experiencing these in your presence right now, would you consider them rational and logical? Identify the cognitive distortions that may be involved and write them next to the erroneous belief.

_____

_____

Step 3: Take the distorted belief or thought and reconstruct it into a true and positive statement. Avoid using any negative terms.

_____

_____

THREE ASPECTS OF RATIONAL BELIEFS

Thinking consistently rational thoughts will enhance emotional intelligence. The following three rules for rational thinking are based on the Rational Behavioral Therapy model by noted psychologist Maxie Maultsby. In order for a thought to be completely rational, it must have ALL three.

1. **The thought must be accurate and true.** That means it is based on obvious fact. It is helpful here to know the cognitive distortions. Analyze your thoughts for those distortions and correct the distortion(s) identified.

2. **Rational thinking best helps you to achieve your wisely developed short-term and long-term goals.** It's good to take some time to develop those goals. Wise goals will protect you from harm, prevent unwanted conflict with others, and lead to a healthier you.

3. **Rational thinking causes progression toward appropriate and desired feelings** without resorting to alcohol and drugs or other bad habits for short-term "relief". Some have translated this step to mean feeling the way you want to feel. When it is healthful and appropriate to feel calm, yet you feel angry and upset, you need to go back to the above two aspects of a rational thought, because something is wrong with your thinking. If it is appropriate and healthful to feel sad (over a significant loss or disappointment) and that feeling leads to the development of new rational goals—you are doing correct thinking. (**Note:** *sometimes appropriate feelings are uncomfortable.*)[6]

Action Step 4.4   Rational Thinking

Analyze the last time you were feeling far different than you desired your feelings to be.

A. What were you thinking that made you feel that way? (By definition, you were not thinking rationally. What was your irrational thought?)

_____

B. Was the thought accurate? Look for possible distortions in that thought.

_____

C. Was the thought helping you to achieve your goals? ○ **yes** ○ **no**

 Can you see a problem with either B or C? ○ **yes** ○ **no**

If yes, correct your thought. _____

If no, then you need further help because your thoughts are causing you to feel different than you want to feel.

Example: Your employee does not show up for work, again. She is very important in today's work schedule. When she is at work, she is an excellent employee. But this is now the second time she has failed to show up without notice. You feel extremely upset and angry. With those emotions, now is the time to review the three aspects of a rational thought.

Do you desire to feel upset and angry?

You may not want to feel angry and upset to the degree that you do, but you may still want to express concern, being motivated to achieve your goals for a more efficient cohesive workforce in your company. But, you are extremely upset and angry because you think you absolutely NEED her today and she is not answering any of her phones. But let's look at that thought. What is a need and what is a want? You do need water, air, and sufficient warmth but you don't absolutely need her to be at work today in order for you or your employees to live. This accurate thought helps you to be closer to feeling calm. When you feel closer to calm (as opposed to very upset) it helps your brain to be in a better position to do something wise about her absence at work. Why don't you want to feel completely calm? Because if you are completely calm you are likely to ignore this situation to the extent that you don't address it, therefore potentially adversely affecting you, your employees and your company in the future.

Analyzing this situation further, if you continue to feel too upset you may call the employee and fire her on the spot. There can be two problems to this approach:

Problem 1: *She may have gotten in an accident while driving to work and consequently is not in a position to make a call. Later, others find out that you got angry and fired someone while in a great distress NOT of her own making. Your reputation as a boss will likely go down significantly with that action.*

Problem 2: *There are very few people with her skills to fill the position and it will be difficult to find someone with her skill set to train in a month or more to fill her position. This can cause a greater hindrance to you to achieve your goals for your company.*

A wiser course of action can be to take the employee aside and find out what is happening in her life. Let her know you cannot continue to run this company smoothly with this type of behavior being repeated. You may find that she is in need of this 8-week program that you are now attending. By convincing her to take two hours a week and do some additional reading in the evening, her life can be greatly enhanced. As a result it will not be only her who will benefit, but also you, your employees, and your company. Rational re-thinking not only saved her job, but ultimately may have saved yours. In addition, your re-thinking of rational thoughts helped you to wisely deal with her real underlying problems that were affecting her work performance, which led you to be the "change agent" in enhancing someone else's life.

📅 Organize Your Life

Have any distortions kept you from cleaning your house, car, office, etc.?

» Help yourself eliminate all-or-nothing thinking by taking small steps to accomplish your goal, e.g. straighten one drawer at a time.

» Put aside the thought of overgeneralization that you will never get your house cleaned correctly. Begin one simple step at a time, one project at a time, one room at a time.

» Watch out for emotional reasoning, "I don't feel like cleaning the house;" go ahead put your emotions behind and get it done.

» Be careful not to label yourself as a bad housekeeper. Stay focused and work-through each room with confidence, changing your thoughts and the looks of your house.

» Instead of creating a magnification about the dishes piled high, start washing them knowing that using your hands improves the frontal lobe of the brain.

» When you accomplish a clean environment, avoid disqualifying the positive; when someone compliments you, just say "thank you!"

10 Cognitive Distortions — Answer key to Action Step 4.2

All–or–nothing thinking	There is no "in between." It's completely one way or the other.	8
Overgeneralization	Using limited factual evidence to hold a firm belief that actually is not true.	5
Mental filter	Singling out one aspect of a situation to the complete exclusion of others that should be considered.	6
Mind reading	Having the certainty of knowing what another person is thinking without having to ask.	9
Fortune teller error	Knowing that if THIS happens, THAT will definitely occur.	2
Magnification/Minimization	Majoring in minors and minoring in majors.	1
Personalization	You are totally responsible for the good or bad that happens to you.	10
Emotional Reasoning	Your feelings don't lie.	7
Labeling/Mislabeling	Habitually defining ourselves or others with a descriptive term.	4
Disqualifying the positive	Acknowledging the good, appearing to be objective, but believing the good side has no value.	3

This is the halfway point for our eight-week program. Full recovery can take up to 20 weeks and each person's depression is as individual as he or she is. The most important thing is: **NEVER GIVE UP!**

MAKING AND STAYING WITH POSITIVE LIFESTYLE CHOICES

5

DURING THIS SESSION YOU WILL LEARN:

How to move through the stages of change

The effects of any addiction on the brain

Strengths you can develop to help you change

CNN REPORT ON HAPPINESS[1]

The next time you are deciding between ice cream and cake, buying a car or taking a trip to Europe, accepting a new job or keeping your old one, you should remember two things:

» First, your decision is rooted in the _____ ✎ 5-a to become happy—or at least happier than you are now

» Second, there's a good chance the decision you make will be wrong

» Harvard psychologist Daniel Gilbert summed up our failings this way: "People have a lot of bad theories about happiness."

» Our culture implores us to buy bigger, newer, better things, but research shows "stuff" does not buy happiness. By and large, money buys happiness only for those who lack the basic needs.

» "Once you pass an income of $50,000, more money doesn't buy much more happiness," Gilbert said.

» "We should pass on buying lottery tickets and find small things we can do every day that bring us joy, whether it's going for a walk or cooking a meal or reading a good book."

—NANCY SEGAL

EFFECTS OF HAPPINESS[2]

In an experiment that exposed healthy volunteers to a cold or flu virus, researchers found that happy people were less likely to fall ill.

» Cohen and his colleagues found that based on objective measures of nasal woes, happy people were less likely to develop a cold

» When _____ ✎ 5-b folks did develop a cold, their self-rated symptoms were less severe than would be expected based on objective measures

» When the researchers weighed other factors that could

A merry heart doeth good like a medicine: but a broken spirit drieth the bones.

—PROVERBS 17:22

_____

_____

_____

_____

_____

_____

_____

_____

_____

_____

_____

_____

_____

_____

_____

explain the relationship–like volunteers' perception of their general health, their self-esteem and tendency to be optimistic–happiness itself still seemed to protect against cold symptoms

THE TEN "HIT" CATEGORIES

1. Frontal Lobe
2. Lifestyle
3. Circadian Rhythm
4. Nutrition
5. Toxins
6. Social/Inadequate Coping/Grief
7. _____ 🔑 5-c
8. Medical Condition
9. Developmental
10. Genetic

STAGES OF CHANGE[3]

1. Precontemplation
2. Contemplation
3. Preparation
4. Action
5. Maintenance
6. Termination

DANGERS OF IGNORING INSPIRATION AND/OR SCIENCE

Because there is no immediate consequences to harmful behavior, the harmful behavior is thought to be harmless, or even desirable.

SOLOMON'S STORY

» "Many envied the popularity and abundant glory of Solomon, thinking that of all men he must be the most happy.

» But amid all that glory of artificial display the man envied is the one to be most pitied.

Making positive lifestyle choices ultimately leads to success, happiness, and fulfilment.

1. Unconsciously Incompetent
2. Consciously Incompetent
3. Consciously Competent
4. Unconsciously Competent

Because sentence against an evil work is not executed speedily, therefore the heart of the sons of men is fully set in them to do evil.

—ECCLESIASTES 8:11

» His countenance is dark with despair. All the splendor about him is but to him mockery of the distress and anguish of his _____ ✎5-d as he reviews his misspent life in seeking for happiness through indulgence and selfish gratification of every desire.

» By his own bitter experience, Solomon learned the emptiness of a life that seeks in earthly things its highest good. Gloomy and soul-harassing thoughts troubled him night and day.

» For him there was no longer any joy of life or peace of mind, and the future was dark with despair."

—CONFLICT AND COURAGE 194

ADDICTIONS THAT CAN LEAD TO DEPRESSION/ANXIETY

» Alcohol

» Narcotics

» Benzodiazepines

» Cocaine/Amphetamines

» Sugar

» Chocolate

» Gambling

» Entertainment television or movies

» PSP or video games

» Techno addict

» Entertainment internet

» Facebook

» Caffeine

» Sports

» Syncopated rhythm music

» Pornography

» Deviant sexual practices

» Cutting

[1] I said in mine heart, Go to now, I will prove thee with mirth, therefore enjoy pleasure: and, behold, this also is vanity. [10] And whatsoever mine eyes desired I kept not from them, I withheld not my heart from any joy;... [17] Therefore I hated life;... [20] Therefore I went about to cause my heart to despair...

—ECCLESIASTES 2:1, 10, 17, 20

_____

_____

_____

_____

_____

_____

_____

_____

_____

MAKING AND STAYING WITH POSITIVE LIFESTYLE CHOICES, part 2

COMMON CHARACTERISTICS OF ADDICTIONS

1. Overwhelming compulsion to continually use
2. Need for increased amounts
3. Dependence (withdrawal)
4. High tendency to relapse
5. Detrimental effect on individual/society

TECHNOLOGY ADDICTION[4]

» Technology might be just as addictive as alcohol and drugs and could also wreak havoc with personal and work relationships

» Psychologists specializing in addiction have classified "_____ ✎ 5-e addiction" as an impulse disorder that can be as socially damaging as alcoholism, gambling, and drug addiction.

» Warning signs include using:

> Using text messages, or email when face-to-face interaction would be more appropriate

> Limiting time with friends and family to tend to your email, or to surf the Internet

PORNOGRAPHY EXPOSURE EFFECTS AFTER SIX WEEKS[5]

» Less interested in or attracted to their partner

» More self-absorbed

» Less empathy for others

» Very self-centered world

» Shuts down emotionally

Other Proven Effects of Pornography

» Less pleasure in other interests

» Decrease in motivation

» Increased Irritability with the usual nuisances of life

» Increase in anxiety

» Reduced impulse control

» Lessened ability to foresee consequences

Do not bite at the bait of pleasure, till you are sure there is no hook beneath it.

—THOMAS JEFFERSON

» As Dr. Zillman has said: "The negative effects of pornography have been more consistently proven than the links between smoking and lung cancer."

FALSE WAY OF ALTERING THE WAY YOU FEEL

You can never get enough of what you don't need, because what you don't need will never satisfy you!

OVERCOMING ADDICTIONS REQUIRES UNDERSTANDING OF TEMPERANCE

» Moderation in the use of _____ ✎ 5-f substances

» Abstinence (complete) from unhealthy substances

WHY ABSTINENCE FROM THE UNHEALTHY?

» First, because it is unhealthy

» Second, because of the addictive nature of unhealthy substances

THE CALL FOR MODERATION

» A person who has a compulsive relationship can no more use it "moderately" than an alcoholic can return to moderate drinking or a nicotine addict can return to moderate smoking

» In dealing with any addictive habit, total abstinence for life is necessary

» We have the ability to choose our own pleasures

» If we reward ourselves with a bad habit periodically, we undermine our ability to develop enjoyment for a lifestyle that is free of that agent

...make not provision for the flesh, to fulfill the lusts thereof.

—ROMANS 13:14

...he that endureth to the end shall be saved.

—MATTHEW 10:22

WHAT ABOUT JUST ONCE A MONTH?

» Certainly an improvement, but the desire is being kept alive

» Desire may even be increased, giving rise to feelings of a deep distressing sense of deprivation

» If the addiction is permanently abandoned and the thoughts directed toward the joy of being free, the addiction will soon not be missed

OVERCOMING ADDICTION

» Need to have knowledge that the habit is destructive

» Need to choose to overcome

» Need to _____ ✎ 5-g on spiritual resources

» Let go, and let God

PETER'S LADDER

Faith → Virtue → Knowledge → Temperance → _____ ✎ 5-h
→ Godliness → Brotherly Kindness → Agape Love

HOW TO HELP OTHERS TO CHANGE PERMANENTLY

The most powerful change agent is empathy.

POSITIVE LIFESTYLE CHANGE

» Accept the call

» Rely on spiritual resources

» Change now and forever

If you fail... analyze why.

What were the behaviors and thoughts that led up to ultimate failure?

How can you put these mistakes up as beacons of warning so that you don't go there again?

_____

_____

_____

_____

_____

_____

_____

_____

_____

_____

_____

⚙ What You Learned

» Change is a struggle that requires commitment

» Alcohol, tobacco, caffeine, pornography, technology, cutting, and even some medications can be habit forming and cause an addiction

» You can turn defeat into victory

» Overcoming an addiction is achieved through steps

Reading Prescription

» *Depression: the Way Out,* chapter 7

» Chapter in the book of Proverbs that corresponds with each day's date

» *SOS Help for Emotions: Managing Anxiety, Anger and Depression*–by now you should be finished reading this book, but if you have not, try to finish it this week

» *Telling Yourself the Truth,* chapters 9 and 10

LIFESTYLE IN ACTION

Stage 1: Unconsciously Incompetent (Pre-contemplation)

Stage 2: Consciously Incompetent (Contemplation and Preparation)

Stage 3: Consciously Competent (Action and Maintenance)

Stage 4: Unconsciously Competent (Termination: sticking to the plan)

Stage 5: Termination (You've got it made! Struggle is over. Victory!)

The Stages of Change

The Stages of Change show that, for most people, a change in behavior occurs gradually, moving from being uninterested, unaware, or unwilling to make a change (pre-contemplation), to considering a change (contemplation), to deciding and preparing to make a change. Genuine, determined action is then taken and, over time, attempts are made to maintain the new behavior. Relapses, if they occur, can become part of the process of working toward lifelong change.

1. **Unconsciously Incompetent**

   In Stage 1, you are unaware of the negative effects of your actions. To move from this stage you must be informed and obtain knowledge.

2. **Consciously Incompetent**

   In Stage 2, you gain new knowledge. For example, as a frequent caffeine-user, you learn that caffeine is bad for you. Now that you realize caffeine is damaging your brain, you are aware of the consequences of your actions. Although you have not implemented a change at this point, you are conscious of the fact that you need change.

3. **Consciously Competent**

   In Stage 3, you make the change and stop using caffeine. You rely upon God for strength, and do what you can to change. You consciously take the time to choose a caffeine free item—you think about it before consuming it. During this stage, you may think you are over your addiction, but a series of mistakes can pull you back into a spiral of disaster. You realize the advantage of committing to this new lifestyle for the rest of your life.

4. **Unconsciously Competent**

   In Stage 4, your behavior is becoming more of your unconscious habit and part of your life and you experience the benefits of change. Others often recognize the difference in you. Once you reach this stage, you never want to go back to the old way of life. You are satisfied and fulfilled with the effort it took to get to this point.

5. **Termination**

   Remember... many successful changers go through the stages three or four times before they make it through the cycle of change without at least one slip. Many will return to the contemplation stage of change. Slips give us the opportunity to learn and grow. Never give up!

Action Step 5.1 — Overcoming Addictions

a. Admitting that you have a problem is always the first step to overcoming it. Whether you're dealing with such addictions as alcohol, tobacco, deviant sexual practices, pornography, and drugs, or addiction to nail bitting, media, shopping, and sports, now it's time to make a plan for quitting. Seek help and prepare yourself for obstacles you'll surely encounter.

b. List up to 5 addictions that you would like to overcome, and the benefits of quitting each:

Addictions

1. _____
2. _____
3. _____
4. _____
5. _____

Benefits of Quitting

1. _____
2. _____
3. _____
4. _____
5. _____

c. Starting today, choose at least one addiction that you would like to eliminate.

I will stop: _____   on: _____

   Addiction(s)   *Day / Date*

Ways to Kick the Habit

1. Choose to stop your addiction.

2. Discard addictive substance.

3. Practice deep breathing.

4. Engage in daily exercise (i.e. walking).

5. Get more sleep.

6. Use water inside and outside (drinking water and hydrotherapy).

7. Eliminate heavy meals and heavily spiced foods.

8. Avoid high-risk situations such as: special chairs or place associated with using the harmful substance, work breaks, people who have the same addiction.

If you fail in overcoming your addiction on your own–don't give up! Studies show the more times you seriously try, the more likely you are to succeed. 5-HTP 1000 mg or more (up to twice as much) taken orally in the evening is helpful in giving up tobacco and may possibly help with other addictions. You may want to try Lavella or Lavender oil which can help with anxiety. In addition, remember, if you are willing to take up the "cross" of self-sacrifice (refusing to feed your own harmful desires) and ask God to help you, He will, and success will be achieved.

Action Step 5.2 — Steps to Overcoming Addictions

a. Avoid negative influences. Resist peer pressure, it can wear you down. Stay away from people and places that encourage you to feed your addiction. What feeds your addiction?

_____

b. If needed, get additional help. Once you tell someone, allow others to assist you in getting the help you need. They can coach you through the decisions to change your lifestyle and learn new coping mechanisms. Who can be your coach?

_____

c. Sign a contract. Write an agreement with a counselor, parent, or pastor, saying you will not abuse technology anymore. This gives meaning and a sense of urgency, holding you accountable to your decision to come clean. Who will you ask to hold you accountable?

_____

d. Develop a support team. If old feelings and habits start to creep back in, request help from family, friends, and other resources to keep you on track. Who will be your support team?

_____

66

I can do all things through Christ who strengthens me.

—PHILIPPIANS 4:13

Action Step 5.3 — Review

Review the previous four weeks Lifestyle in Action sections. Seriously evaluate yourself using the following scale, choosing the appropriate letter (A, B, or C). The number in parenthesis indicates the session where each is found.

A. *I have habitually changed/added/been consistent with these activities.*

B. *I have half-heartedly changed or added these activities to my schedule.*

C. *I have yet to change or add these activities to my weekly routine.*

	A	B	C	*Write out a plan (with a day/date) for each Lifestyle in Action point you need to adopt:*
① No critical or negative speech (1)	○	○	○	
② Adequate water intake (1)	○	○	○	
③ Exercise and interval training (1, 2)	○	○	○	
④ Classical music therapy (1)	○	○	○	
⑤ Deep breathing exercises (2)	○	○	○	
⑥ Light therapy; good light exposure (2)	○	○	○	
⑦ Massage (2)	○	○	○	
⑧ Contrast showers (2)	○	○	○	
⑨ Tryptophan intake (3)	○	○	○	
⑩ Vitamin B_{12} intake (3)	○	○	○	
⑪ Omega-3 intake (3)	○	○	○	
⑫ Folic acid intake (3)	○	○	○	
⑬ Cholesterol intake reduced/eliminated (3)	○	○	○	
⑭ Plant-based diet (3)	○	○	○	
⑮ Analyze your thoughts for distortions (4)	○	○	○	
⑯ Reconstructing your thoughts (4)	○	○	○	

The new behavior must be practiced over time to create a new habit.

🗓 Organize Your Life

» Share with others in the group what area you are going to declutter this week.

» Start decluttering your home of addictive substances (caffeinated products, chocolates, cigarettes, alcohol; move your computer to a public part of the house if it is a problem for you, etc.).

» Rearrange furniture to break addictive habits (i.e. your favorite chair to sit in while smoking).

» Set a timer and spend 15 minutes decluttering, even if you have to break it down into 5-minute segments.

» Rule of thumb: if you have any two items and you only need one, get rid of the least desirable.

» Spend at least 5 minutes a day clearing a path in your worst room. (You know, the place you would never allow anyone to see.)

STRESS WITHOUT DISTRESS

6

DURING THIS SESSION YOU WILL LEARN:

The five emotional wounds

How to avoid the potential effects of loneliness

How to cope with stress

STRESS AND STRESSORS

» Pressures from the outside

» Stress is your response to stressors

REACTIONS TO STRESSORS

» PHASE 1–Alarm reaction

» PHASE 2–State of _____ ⚲ 6-a

» PHASE 3–Stage of exhaustion

SOCIAL HITS INCREASE THE RISK OF DEPRESSION AND ANXIETY[1-8]

» Absence of social support

» Negative, stressful life events

» Grandparents who raise their grandchildren

» Immediate family member that you live with is an alcoholic or drug addict

» Suffered critical loss, such as a loved one or treasured job within the last 18 months

» Multiple relationship threats/issues

LONELINESS AND DEPRESSION

People with depression often seek isolation due to common distorted thoughts.

» "People drain me, even the closest of friends, and I find loneliness to be the best state in the union to live in."
—MARGARET CHO

» "It's so lonely when you don't even know yourself."
—HILLEL SLOVAK

And the Lord God said, it is not good that the man should be alone...
—GENESIS 2:18

When we truly realize that we are all alone is when we need others the most.
—RONALD ANTHONY

Distortion: the events in my life have caused my depression and anxiety, so to do better I must limit future events.

_____

_____

_____

_____

» "If you are lonely when you are alone, you are in bad company."

—JEAN-PAUL SARTRE

» "With some people solitariness is an escape not from others but from themselves. For they see in the eyes of others only a reflection of themselves."

—ERIC HOFFER

POTENTIAL COMPLICATIONS OF LONELINESS

» "The person who tries to live alone will not succeed as a human being. His heart withers if it does not answer another heart. His mind shrinks away if he hears only the echoes of his own thoughts and finds no other inspiration."

—PEARL S. BUCK

» "When so many are lonely as seem to be lonely, it would be inexcusably selfish to be lonely alone."

—TENNESSEE WILLIAMS

» "When people are lonely they stoop to any companionship."

—LEW WALLACE

» "If you are afraid of being lonely, don't try to be right."

—JULES RENARD

» "What loneliness is more lonely than distrust?"

—T.S. ELIOT

» "I've got everything I need except a man. And I'm not one of those women who thinks a man is the answer to everything, but I'm tired of being alone."

—UNKNOWN AUTHOR

» "The dread of loneliness is greater than the fear of bondage, so we get married."

—CYRIL CONNOLLY

Potential risks of being alone and being lonely:

» Lack of success

» Choosing anyone who will befriend you to get close to you

» Truth is de-valued

» Become more distrustful of others

» Get married to just about anyone who will marry you

_____

_____

_____

_____

_____

_____

_____

_____

_____

ABC EXAMPLE[9]

A—Activating Event
"Oh, the phone is ringing again! I haven't answered it all day."

B—Belief
"The phone should not be ringing! It's always a problem when someone calls. It might be something I can't stand to handle, something horrible."

C—Consequence
"I haven't talked on the phone today and I'm not going to start now. I'm too upset and tired to talk to anyone, anyway. Why is life so difficult? I'm starting to feel nauseated!"

D—Dispute
"What law says the phone must not ring? To say it is always a problem when the phone rings is overgeneralizing and exaggerating."

» "I can stand talking on the phone, and I can handle even unpleasant situations."

» "I am not going to demand my life be stress free!"

THE ADVANTAGES OF BEING ALONE

» "Better be alone than in bad company."
—THOMAS FULLER

» "They are never alone that are accompanied with noble thought."
—SIR PHILIP SIDNEY

» "It would do the world good if every man would compel himself occasionally to be absolutely alone. Most of the world's progress has come out of such loneliness."
—BRUCE BARTON

The worthwhile desire is to stop our distorted thinking, not to stop the events of life.

I don't like it. I don't like it.
It's o.k. It's o.k.
I can stand it anyway.
I can stand it anyway.
I'm alright. I'm alright.

(to the tune of *Frère Jacques*)

There are far worse things than being alone.

EMOTIONAL WOUND #1

» _____ 🔧 6-b

» We have made errors in thinking and errors in doing

» Often gets infected and abscessed

» If no remedy, will result in septic shock which is an alternatingly painful with euphoric death (the death alternates between pain and a state of euphoria)

» False sympathizers are serial killers

THE ABSCESSED AND INFECTED (SELF-INFLICTED) WOUND REMEDY

» Needs (surgery)

» Need another wound to heal the original wound

» Requires the willingness to suffer more pain

» Ask for forgiveness and as far as possible right the wrongs

EMOTIONAL WOUND #2

» Imaginary wound

> Feel slighted

> Chip on the shoulder

» Caused by the cognitive distortion of magnification

» The magnification of self

The pain of humility is far less than the painful effects of arrogance.

Often people waste time and energy in ruminating on perceived wounds that have NOT adversely affected their ability to achieve their goals. Such wounds are imaginary.

SYMPTOMS OF PRIDE[10]

- » Trying to be noticed
- » Craving attention
- » Itching for compliments
- » Needing to be important
- » Detesting the idea of being submissive
- » Loathing the idea of admitting to wrongdoing
- » Strongly opinionated
- » Being argumentative
- » Demanding your way

- » Wanting control over others
- » Flaunting your individual rights
- » Refusing advice
- » Being critical, yet resenting criticism
- » Being _____ 6-c
- » Thinking you have excellences you don't have

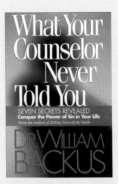

The book of Clinical Psychologist William Backus reveals the seven "sins" that lead to mental illness, how to recognize them, and how they can be eliminated.

❝

Let all bitterness, wrath, anger, clamour, and evil speaking, be put away from you, with all malice: And be ye kind one to another, tenderhearted, forgiving one another, even as God for Christ's sake hath forgiven you.

—APOSTLE PAUL

STRESS WITHOUT DISTRESS, part 2

EMOTIONAL WOUND #3

» Vengeful injury

» Other people's intentional mistakes combined with hatred

STUDIES ON RESENTMENT, ANGER AND HOSTILITY[11-17]

» Increased blood pressure

» Increased cardiovascular disease

» Increased rates of infection

» Possibly increases the risk of cancer

» May hasten cancer death

» Increased depression, anxiety

» Decrease in life satisfaction

TO ERR IS HUMAN AND TO FORGIVE DIVINE[18, 19]

Among survey participants of all ages, however, reports of forgiveness were associated with decreased psychological distress, including feelings of restlessness, hopelessness, and nervousness.

» Not all forgiving is immediately beneficial

» Proactive forgiveness—asking for forgiveness, rather than granting it—was associated with increased psychological distress among all study participants

» Other acts of proactive forgiveness would include asking God's forgiveness for hurting someone or praying for someone who has hurt them

Blessed are the merciful: for they shall obtain mercy.

—MATTHEW 5:7

» "Simply put, harboring a grudge is stressful. The body has "sub-systems" designed to deal with stressors, but constantly putting them to the test can inflict some "wear-and-tear."

» "Habitual anger, hostility, and anxiety are linked to a higher risk of heart problems. People who routinely ruminate over past wrongs "chip away" at their physical health."

—WITVLIET

To measure the short-term effects of forgiveness and grudge-holding, Witvliet and her colleagues studied 71 men and women who described an experience in which a friend, family member, or partner hurt them.

» They then had to follow scripts that simulated two conditions

» In the "grudge condition," participants were prompted to "rehearse the hurt" and think about how the offenders should suffer for their transgressions

» The "forgiveness condition" prompted participants to empathize with the offender and _____ ✎ 6-d that they, too, have hurt others

» The researchers found that when participants harbored grudges they reported more negative feelings, anger, sadness and a lack of control

» What's more, their heart rates and blood pressure rose, and they showed greater nervous system activity

» While forgiveness was linked to better physical functioning in this study, Witvliet emphasized that it is important for people to know what true forgiveness is

» The study participants were not asked to excuse or ignore the behavior of those who hurt them, but instead take a "_____" ✎ 6-e toward them

Serenity Prayer
God grant me the serenity to accept the things I cannot change,
The courage to change the things I can,
And the wisdom to know the difference.

_____
_____
_____
_____
_____
_____
_____
_____
_____
_____
_____
_____

REMEDY FOR EMOTIONAL WOUND #3 HUMAN

» Forgiveness

» Experience God's love (and mercy)

EMOTIONAL WOUND #4

» Accidental injury

» Errors and cognitive distortions would be bad enough if it just affected the individual who is mistaken, but it nearly always adversely effects innocent individuals

REMEDY FOR ACCIDENTAL INJURY

» Recognize that just because it is an accident and unintended consequences occurred, the set-up for it to occur still happened

» Thus forgiveness is necessary for healing

» "Father, forgive them, for they know not what they do."

—LUKE 23:34

» The demonstration of mercy

UNFAIR?[20]

» Everything is as it should be at every given moment, although it might not be the way we want it to be

» For a situation to occur, everything that is necessary for it to occur must be present, or it will not happen

» _____ ✎ 6-f "should statements" insist that reality conform to one's desires or demands, rather than our desires conforming to reality

If you don't want to be corrected, you are denying yourself the opportunity to improve.

Don't let the slights and nuances of life get you down.

EMOTIONAL WOUND #5

REPROOF

"Let the righteous smite me; it shall be a kindness: and let him reprove me; it shall be an excellent oil that won't damage me."

— PSALM 141:5

LEARN FROM YOUR ENEMIES

"Reprove not a scorner, lest he hate thee: rebuke a wise man, and he will love thee. Give instruction to a wise man, and he will be yet wiser: teach a just man, and he will increase in learning."

—PROVERBS 9:8, 9

ABC EXAMPLE[21]

» **A.** Activating event:

› "My boss said my nose is too big!"

» **B.** Beliefs and self-talk statements:

› "He has no right to talk to me that way! He must not, he should not have insulted me. He's a fool! I can't stand him saying that."

» **C.** Consequences—emotional and behavioral:

› "I feel mad and angry. I might slap him. I might tell him off and demand an apology."

» **D.** Dispute:

› "Wait a minute. I am making myself mad. He doesn't control my anger; I do. I am annoyed but I don't have to get angry. I'd _____ ✎ 6-g that he wouldn't talk to me that way. But I'm responsible for my own anger. I will exhibit a spirit of mercy towards him."

How to know whether it is a need or a want: how long can I go without this before I die?

It's good to know people that are NOT our friends. Those people are more likely to tell us some truths about us that are unpleasant. That gives us an opportunity to correct our unpleasantness.

Trusting in someone who is larger than you and cares for you is part of a comprehensive stress control strategy.

HOW TO RECOGNIZE AND REMEDY EMOTIONAL WOUND #5 (REBUKE OR REPROOF)

» Are there any elements of truth (areas that I can improve upon in the future) that led to this wounding?

» If my best friend said this to me, would I still feel wounded?

CONFUSING NEEDS WITH WANTS

» Air, water, food, sufficient warmth, God

» To have a certain appearance

» To have things go our way

» To have an outstanding job

» To be liked by everybody

» Perfection

» New car

WATCH OUT FOR FORTUNE TELLER ERROR

» Catastrophizing

» Magical worry

EXAMPLES OF STRESS CONTROL

"Of the Jews five times received I forty stripes save one. Thrice was I beaten with rods, once was I stoned, thrice I suffered shipwreck, a night and a day I have been in the deep; In journeyings often, in perils of waters, in perils of robbers, in perils by mine own countrymen, in perils by the heathen, in perils in the city, in perils in the wilderness, in perils in the sea, in perils among false brethren; in weariness and painfulness, in watchings often, in hunger and thirst, in fastings often, in cold and nakedness."

—2 CORINTHIANS 11:24-27

We are troubled on every side, yet not distressed; we are perplexed, but not in despair; persecuted, but not forsaken; cast down, but not destroyed.

—2 CORINTHIANS 4:8, 9

Yet in all these things we are more than conquerors through Him who loved us.

— ROMANS 8:37

Catastrophizing
Frequently thinking of worse case scenarios.

Magical Worry
If I don't worry about this, the worst may happen. So worry, I must!

⚙ What You Learned

- » How we cope with stress has a lot to do with how we respond to the "wounds" that life can bring

- » How arrogance and pride leads to emotional wounds

- » The difference between a need and a want

Reading Prescription

- » *Depression: the Way Out,* chapter 8

- » Chapter in the book of Proverbs that corresponds with each day's date

- » *Telling Yourself the Truth,* chapters 11 and 12

LIFESTYLE IN ACTION

A healthy lifestyle can help you cope with stress. Part of a healthy lifestyle is getting restorative and efficient sleep. This helps your brain produce more melatonin, a very potent antioxidant that helps you cope with stress and helps you experience more pleasure the next day. To produce enough melatonin, you have to get enough tryptophan/carbohydrates from food sources that are mentioned in chapter 4 of *Depression: the Way Out* ("Healthy food, better mood"). You also have to get bright enough light, preferably early in the morning, to set your body clock and produce enough serotonin in order to make enough melatonin at night. Vitamin D and calcium along with sleeping in a dark environment help this process along.

If you are troubled by negative thoughts, it would be wise to examine your bedtime routine. Studies show that people who go to bed later and sleep for shorter periods of time often experience more repetitive negative thoughts than others, even if they are a self-proclaimed "night-owl." A simple shift in your circadian rhythm could be an easy and inexpensive solution to persistent negative thoughts. Adopting an "early to bed, early to rise" lifestyle is considered by some to be the "new Prozac."[22]

Screen Time and Sleep

One way to promote good sleep at night, and support the effort for an earlier bedtime, is to avoid the use of screens in the hours before sleep. Researchers have found that viewing a glowing screen can disrupt the body's natural sleep patterns, including decreased levels of the night-time hormone melatonin, and later timing of the circadian clock. When experiment participants read an electronic book before bed rather than a print book, they took nearly ten minutes longer to fall asleep and had lower REM sleep as well as reduced alertness in the morning. The screen time was shown to have an "extremely powerful effect" that can result in negative consequences to frontal lobe function.[23]

Action Step 6.1   Dealing With Stressors

List the top 5 things that cause you to feel stressed and threaten your ability to cope. Then list why each is a problem, and write a potential solution that could help the situation. You can list stressors (outside influences that cause you to feel stressed) or include stressors that have to do with your own thoughts.

Stressor *(Dog barks through the night)*	Problem *(Interrupts sleep)*	Solution *(Wear ear plugs)*
1. _____	1. _____	1. _____
2. _____	2. _____	2. _____
3. _____	3. _____	3. _____
4. _____	4. _____	4. _____
5. _____	5. _____	5. _____

Action Step 6.2 — Big Five Stress Reducers

When you are feeling overwhelmed to the point of questioning if you can cope, do all or any of the "Big Five Stress Reducers."

1. Deep breathing

2. Reframing your situation and thoughts

3. Taking an hour-long vigorous walk

4. Listening to relaxing and uplifting classical music

5. Meditation through prayer. The prayer that is most helpful is not trying to change God, but rather praying to God to help you change to better thinking and doing.

Additional Steps to Help With Long Term Stress Control:

1. Maintain a healthy practical schedule that has an hour of free time built in (if you are efficient in your other daily activities) to do things you enjoy, or spend time with your family and friends.

2. Commit to an honorable cause that is morally sound and helps others. If possible, find something you can do as part of a team to get your mind off your troubles and help others in need or distress.

3. After appropriate planning and instituting a healthy schedule (see number 1 above), worrying about the results is counterproductive and not helpful.

4. Dwell on the good.

5. Eliminate caffeine and alcohol.

6. Trust God. Realizing that there is Someone who is larger and more powerful than you, who loves you and wants you to succeed, is part of a healthy stress control plan. Then you can say as did the apostle Paul, "We are troubled on every side, yet not distressed; we are perplexed, but not in despair; persecuted, but not forsaken; cast down, but not destroyed." –2 Corinthians 4:8,9. In fact, despite the significant, and often extreme, stressors in his life he could say, "In all these things we are more than conquerors through him that loved us." –Romans 8:37

Action Step 6.3 — Good Quality Sleep

Listed are additional suggestions for getting good quality sleep. Circle the ones you need to improve.

1. Sleep in a very dark, cool, tidy, comfortable, and quiet environment.

2. Provide fresh air in your sleeping room.

3. Increase exposure to natural light during daylight hours, or get bright light therapy if not able to enjoy natural outdoor light.

4. Set anxieties and worries aside as you get in bed and make sure your conscience is clear.

5. Restrict food intake during the evening meal and don't eat for several hours before bed (three or more preferably).

6. Maintain a regular schedule for bedtime and waking time.

7. Ensure vigorous, daily physical exercise.

8. Make sure that none of the medications you take interfere with sleep.

🗓 Organize Your Life

Stay Organized:

» If you take it, put it back.

» If you drop it, pick it up.

» If you opened it, close it.

» If you use it up, replace it.

Many stressful moments can be avoided if the car keys, purse, and glasses are always kept in the same place.

Plan Ahead:

» By preparing for events well in advance, you can divide up the tasks and decrease overload to maintain only the needed optimal amount of stress. Deadlines can be useful in accomplishing goals.

» Choose an area in your living quarters that often lead to frustration and/or stress. Start organizing it by sorting in categories:

  › Must keep (easy accessible)

  › Occasionally used (store on higher shelves, further back in drawers)

> › Benefiting others (charitable, gifts)

> › Out of circulation (label and move items to another area if limited in space)

> › Junk (garage sale, trash)

Enhance your sleep:

» Make your bed when you get up. Time how long it takes and challenge yourself to do it in under 60 seconds. The room looks nicer and it is more appealing when going to bed at night.

» Have two sets of sheets. When you strip your bed (at least once a week) you can make the bed immediately and not have to wait for the dirty sheets to be laundered and dried.

» Use a nightlight that will not affect your circadian rhythm. Having a good nightlight will help you avoid turning on the lights while still being able to get around at night.

Take care of finances:

Strained finances can significantly increase your stress level. Listed are suggestions to help with your stress management:

» Make and stick to a budget.

» Avoid late payments and pay the entire monthly balance on any credit card statements.

» Reconcile and categorize expenses monthly, in part to keep up with your budget.

» Live within your means. Consider paying cash instead of using credit cards.

» Quit paying for things that are addictive and harmful.

» Save 5-10% of your income.

» Have a "piggy" bank for small bills and change. Slowly, it can add up to a significant amount.

» Give a minimum of 10% of your income to a worthy charity.

» For a long-term financial strategy, invest in education:

> › A 6-month certificate may help you gain a promotion or a job you prefer with higher pay.

> › An additional four years of education may double your income.

» Keep up with your mail: immediately sort payments, statements, junk mail, educational, and religious materials into proper bins as you open mail.

» Keep your bills to pay, envelopes, stamps, and return address labels in one place (a basket, desk, etc.).

OVERCOMING LOSS

7

DURING THIS SESSION YOU WILL LEARN:

The stages of grief

Learn the tasks of mourning that bring healing

Understand the process of healthy grieving

EMOTIONAL WOUND #6

» Doing our job—unexplained loss

» The example of Job

» In this imperfect world, life will be unfair at times

» It's OK not to know why

» Don't jump to conclusions

DEFINITIONS

» _____Grief_____ ✎ 7-a: an emotional reaction that follows the loss of someone or something of great value

» Mourning: the psychological process that occurs when you experience loss

TYPES OF LOSSES

» Social status

» Body part

» The ability to maintain a physical function

» Job

» Home

» Loved one

» Vision

LOSS OF A GREAT, LOVING SPOUSE[1]

» Widows and widowers were less likely to regain the same level of happiness they had before the loss, especially if their marriages were satisfying

» Most people who lost a spouse but did not remarry took about _____ ✎ 7-b years to recover emotionally

...My God, my God, why hast thou forsaken me?

—MATTHEW 27:46

How healthfully you live has a lot to do with how well you grow from the inevitable losses of life.

REALITY VS. DISTORTIONS

» "I'm losing an important part of my life."

_____

» "My world has ended."

_____

» "I can't live without her."

_____

» "I will miss the companionship and love that we shared."

_____

» "I will never again be happy because he died. It's unfair."

_____

STAGES OF GRIEF

STAGE 1–SHOCK & DISBELIEF

» Events seem unreal

» Feeling of numbness

» Denial of the loss

» Crying

» Anger, screaming

STAGE 2–DEVELOPING AWARENESS

» Duration of ____3 –12____ ✎ 7-c months

» Preoccupation with the loss

» Anxiety

» Restlessness, difficulty sleeping

> When thinking about companions gone, we feel ourselves doubly alone.
>
> —SIR WALTER SCOTT

> Lonely people, in talking to each other, can make each other lonelier.
>
> —LILLIAN HELLMAN

_____

_____

_____

_____

_____

_____

_____

_____

_____

_____

POSSIBLE CHARACTERISTICS OF STAGE 2

› Loss of appetite

› Digestive problems

› Fatigue

› Anger

› Guilt

› Identification with the lost loved one

› A depressive response on the anniversary of the loss

› A clearer awareness of the loss

› Recognition of the consequences of the loss

› Mood swings

THE GOOD NEWS ABOUT STAGE 2

Although long in duration, you should gradually feel better month by month.

STAGE 3–RESOLUTION

» Duration of 3 to 12 months after the loss

» Incorporation of new habits

» Positive lifestyle changes

THE GOOD NEWS ABOUT STAGE 3

You gradually take charge of your life and resolve the loss through activity, readjustment, and education.

Suffering through a loss gives you the opportunity to develop more character strengths and virtues.

LESSONS OF GRIEF[2]

» Forty men whose immune systems were already compromised were studied from 4 to 9 years after they had experienced _____ ✎ **7-d** loss

» Grief over the loss of a loved one is often followed by introspection, and a reaffirmation of life's worth and meaning

» 65% of the men had engaged in a thoughtful consideration of the meaning of their loved one's death

  › This is a process the authors call "cognitive processing"

» This type of reflection can lead individuals to different conclusions:

  › **GROUP 1:** For some, their loved one's death only emphasized the negative aspects of life

  › **GROUP 2:** Others simply accepted the death and moved on

  › **GROUP 3:** For others, the demise of a loved one led them to a newfound respect for life and a commitment to significantly improve their personal life

» Compared with other subjects, men who discovered this new meaning in life showed significant improvement in immune function

» This group also showed a significant advantage in long term survival

» This research demonstrated that a newfound sense of purpose can boost the body's immune system as it bolsters the spirit

OVERCOMING LOSS

» Recognizing your life has not ended

» Putting the loss in perspective

» What have you learned?

» The five tasks for healthy grieving

When loss occurs, it gives us a choice. It is up to us whether we become bitter or better.

_____
_____
_____
_____
_____
_____
_____
_____
_____
_____
_____
_____
_____
_____
_____
_____
_____
_____

OVERCOMING LOSS, part 2

HEALTHY GRIEVING[3]

» Worden conceptualizes the grief process as

_____ 🔑 7-e

» Tasks imply that there is work to do

» This can be empowering to the mourner who feels so helpless

TASKS OF MOURNING

TASK I: ACCEPT THE REALITY OF THE LOSS

» Communicate about the loss

» Have a mourning ritual

TASK II: WORK THROUGH THE PAIN[4, 5]

» Do not avoid the pain

» Be honest about how you feel

» Write about the loss

» Self-care is important:

› Adequate sleep

› Balanced diet

› Exercise

» Maintaining social ties

› Studies have shown poor social support to be more closely related to later depression than is a history of torture

» Maintaining spiritual ties

Going through the proper steps of healthy grieving can actually improve your immune system and health.

Time does not always heal "wounds," but working through them over time can.

_____

_____

_____

_____

_____

_____

_____

_____

_____

_____

"In the full light of day, and in hearing of the music of other voices, the caged bird will not sing the song that his master seeks to teach him. He learns a snatch of this, a trill of that, but never a separate and entire melody. But the master covers the cage, and places it where the bird will listen to the one song he is to sing. In the dark, he tries and tries again to sing that song until it is learned, and he breaks forth in perfect melody. Then the bird is brought forth, and ever after he can sing that song in the light. Thus God deals with His children. He has a song to teach us, and when we have learned it amid the shadows of affliction we can sing it ever afterward."

—MINISTRY OF HEALING 472

TASK III: ADJUST TO ENVIRONMENT WITH THE LOSS

» Don't make dramatic _____ 🔑 7-f decisions

» Identify the roles that the lost person or thing played in your life

» Find how these functions can best be met now

TASK IV: TO EMOTIONALLY RELOCATE THE LOSS

» This does not mean that the loss is forgotten. Reminiscing helps

» Build on current or new relationships

» Develop new routines

» Find new interests and continue old ones

Patience
Capacity to endure hardship, difficulty, or inconvenience without complaint.
—ROGET'S THESAURUS

The power of suffering with fortitude; uncomplaining endurance of evils or wrongs, as toil, pain, poverty, insult, oppression, calamity, etc.
—AMERICAN HERITAGE DICTIONARY

What choice would you make? To have no potential to ever experience love, with no loss potential?

Or the possibility to experience love, with the possibility to experience loss?

"The greatest of these is love."
—APOSTLE PAUL

TASK V: TO GROW FROM THE LOSS

» Do not settle for surviving

» Honor the lost person or thing by growing from the pain

» Reflect on what you have learned or gained through the loss

» Let life become more _____ ✎ 7-g

» How have you grown from loss?

» What are some ways you can grow from loss?

GRIEF VS DEPRESSION

TASK VI: ACCEPT THE REALITY OF THE LOSS

» Feelings of worthlessness

» Suicidal ideation

» Grossly impaired functioning

» Prolonged bereavement

» Recognizing your life has not ended

TAKE COMFORT

» Loss was never meant to be

» It's a complication of freedom, which is necessary for love

» There is a Creator who has made a plan that we should never experience loss, sadness, or death again

» He is not only Creator, He is Re-Creator

» "...run with patience the race that is set before us."

—HEBREWS 12:1

It's In The Valley I Grow

Sometimes life seems hard to bear,
Full of sorrow, trouble and woe
It's then we have to remember
That it's in the valleys we grow.

If we always stayed on the mountain top
And never experienced pain,
We would never appreciate God's love
And would be living in vain.

We have so much to learn
And our growth is very slow,
Sometimes we need the mountaintops,
But it's in the valleys we grow.

We do not always understand
Why things happen as they do,
But I am very sure of one thing.
My Lord will see me through.

The little valleys are nothing
When we picture Christ on the cross
He went through the valley of death;
His victory was Satan's loss.

Forgive me Lord, for complaining
When I'm feeling so very low.
Just give me a gentle reminder
That it's in the valleys I grow.

Continue to strengthen me, Lord
And use my life each day
To share Your love with others
And help them find their way.

Thank You for the valleys, Lord
For this one thing I know
The mountain tops are glorious
But it's in the valleys I grow!

—JANE EGGLESTON

⚙ What You Learned

» There are many different types of losses

» Healthy mourning moves through the stages of grief without being complicated by major depression

» You should not allow cognitive distortions to creep in and adversely influence the reality of your loss

Reading Prescription

» *Depression: the Way Out,* chapter 6

» Chapter in the book of Proverbs that corresponds with each day's date

» *Telling Yourself the Truth,* chapters 13 and 14

LIFESTYLE IN ACTION

As social beings, it is healthy to obtain support from various significant people in our lives. A loss can be an unexpected blow that threatens the balance of life and makes it more difficult to achieve our goals.

We may experience many different types of losses in our lives. Can you relate to any of the losses below?

» **Loss of a significant person** (death, divorce, illness)

» **Loss of role** (occupation, job, relationship such as parent, child, friend)

» **Loss of home or physical property** (disasters, aging)

» **Loss of moral values** (honesty, courage, self-control, responsibility)

» **Loss of body function** (eyesight, hearing, limbs, mental capacities)

» **Loss of religious beliefs** (questioning beliefs, disillusioned with church)

» **Loss of hope or death of a vision** (miscarriage, infertility, relationship, career)

Learning to deal appropriately with these losses will help maintain a proper equilibrium, prevent depression, and allow for positive growth in developing character strengths.

Action Step 7.1 — **Growing From Loss**

Reflect on a loss you have experienced. List it below *(e.g. Loss of a vision).*

LOSS OF VISION | HEALTH

How did this impact your life? *("My husband and I planned to travel when we retired. His stroke changed everything.")*

MY HUSBAND + I PLANNED TO LIVE
IN SCOTLAND + BUY A HOUSE IN INVERNESS
BUT I BECAME SICK

What beliefs or feelings can you identify in your description above? *("Now we can't do anything! We won't be able to go anywhere ever again.")*

WE CANNOT BUY A HOUSE BECAUSE
I AM UNWELL WITH ANXIETY

Try to understand your experiences in a more clear, accurate, truthful, and positive way. Change your distorted thought into a true statement. For example, instead of thinking, "This changed EVERYTHING! Now we can't do anything!" change your thoughts to, *"Even though our days are filled with therapy to help him recover, we still have time to visit with family and make a difference in their lives, especially our grandchildren. Our travel plans and sight-seeing may take longer because we have to stop to rest, but we can still see many of the destinations we dreamed about."*

IT IS NOT IMPOSSIBLE FOR US TO
BUY A HOUSE

Grow from the loss by turning your focus on the blessings that you currently enjoy or have in your life. Write at least three important things you are thankful for in your life. For example, *"I am grateful to have my husband and his companionship. I can enjoy taking life slower and stopping to smell the roses."*

Overcoming depression and dealing with significant losses requires quality social support. Think of people (family members, friends, or church acquaintances) and activities that contribute to your meaningful social support.

Because of misconceptions, you may find it difficult to feel supported. Research shows that often your circle of friends significantly changes through your grieving process. There is a tendency to filter out friends or family members who were emotionally insensitive, who seemed to lack depth and perspective, or who were simply absent in your time of need.[6]

Ways to Show Support to Others Who are Grieving

1. Spend time listening and allow them to talk or cry.

2. When you listen to their story encourage expression of the facts, details, and emotions related to the loss. Recommend that they write about their loss in a journal.

3. Keep in touch. Say, "I'm just calling to see how you're doing today."

4. Unless you have gone through a very similar loss, refrain from expressions such as, "I know exactly how you feel," "I understand completely," or "At least they're no longer suffering." These expressions can cause the mourner to feel you are minimizing their experience or pain.

Action Step 7.2   Find Encouragement From Loss

Share a meaningful experience that happened during your loss that brought you encouragement:

_____

_____

_____

_____

_____

_____

Conversation Starters

» Introduce yourself and let them know where you are from.

» Tell them how you knew him/her (friend, neighbor, co-worker).

» Ask them to tell you an interesting story about him/her.

» If the person has lost their spouse or parent, you may ask, "What was your most memorable moment together?" (holiday, vacation, etc.)

Action Step 7.3 — Stages of Grief

List the stages of grief:

_____

_____

If you are going through a loss, which stage are you currently in?

_____

_____

Take time to journal about your loss. Write down the positive attributes you remember of the lost thing/person; taking it from your mind and putting on paper helps to grow from the loss. Write about it objectively, like a good news reporter would, then refuse to rehash all of the traumatic details, realizing you have already journaled those details. Also, writing about the positive aspects of your loss can help with the grieving process.

This week, make a point to share your appreciation and gratitude with an individual (teacher, parent, mentor) who has really impacted your life. Let them know in person, by phone, a letter, or e-mail, the positive influence they had on your life. This will help improve your social wellness.

It is especially beneficial to commit yourself to honorable causes that help others. Some suggestions include getting involved in community or church projects, church attendance, and other activities consistent with good goals. Do you have any plans for community involvement? If so, share them with the group.

More on Emotionally Relocating the Loss

One of the important tasks in healthy grieving is emotionally relocating the loss. A loss results in a practical problem if that loss makes it more challenging for you to achieve your goals. Whenever you experience a practical problem, there often is a large emotional reaction to that practical problem. That means your loss resulted in two problems, not just one: a practical problem and an emotional problem.

The emotional problem not only makes you feel miserable (mad, sad, and/or afraid of the future—anxiety) but often can result in even more practical problems occurring due to the paralyzing effects of these severe feelings. (We can add to actual problems by believing that we must feel or act in a certain way. An example would be to believe we have to emotionally react with a certain behavior to a loss instead of calmly grieving. By doing this we can magnify the loss.)

Some people mistakenly believe they must feel horrible, terrible, and awful after a loss, or else they are not "normal" in their grieving. But, these feelings they deem necessary, can actually get in the way of true healthy grieving. The truth is that time cannot go backwards, meaning the loss is there. It is a very important step to realize, "it is what it is."

When you realize that we will have this really bad practical problem whether you are miserable about it or not, then it makes sense to just give up the misery. What a difference this can make! Then, instead of two problems, you only have one. Your bad emotions will be replaced with emotions that are much more towards emotional calm. When you are emotionally calm, not only do you feel better, but you have emotionally relocated the loss and as a result, you are in a much better position to choose a wise course of action to deal with your practical problem. [7]

📅 Organize Your Life

How do you decide to part with things that are a constant reminder of your loss? Listed below are suggestions to help you move forward.

» Instead of saving everything, take pictures of the cherished items. Make a scrapbook and write memories that you or others (family, friend) have relating to the particular item.

» Decide if you will go through the process of sorting the belongings alone or with someone else, such as family member, friend, or professional organizer. Have basic supplies needed for the process such as:

› Boxes or tubs

› Gloves

› Garbage bags

› Markers, paper, sticky notes

› Basic hardware tools

» Divide the sorted items into categories:

› Donations

› Friends

› Family members

› Garage sale

› Trash

» Do the project in stages, as it can be emotionally and physically demanding.

» Be thoughtful in making decisions and check with other family members about certain items that may not matter much to you, but may be meaningful to them.

ENHANCING FRONTAL LOBE FUNCTION

8

DURING THIS SESSION YOU WILL LEARN:

Why your brain is affected by so many things

The positive mental benefits that an antioxidant
plant-based diet imparts

What you can do to protect and enhance your
frontal lobe

THE TEN "HIT" CATEGORIES

1. Frontal Lobe
2. Lifestyle
3. Circadian Rhythm
4. Nutrition
5. Toxins
6. Social
7. Addiction
8. _____ 🔑 8-a
9. Developmental
10. Genetic

COMMON MEDICAL HITS

» Hepatitis C

» Vitamin D deficiency

» Recent head injury

» Stroke

» Terminal cancer

» Parkinson's

» Uncontrolled diabetes

» Lupus

» Congestive heart failure

» Postpartum severe stress

» Premenstrual tension syndrome

» Inadequately treated thyroid disease

» Inadequately treated adrenal gland disease

RESEARCH IN THE 1990s and 2000s

It is now well established that one of the main characteristics of virtually all depressed individuals—no matter what the underlying cause—is a significant decrease in the frontal lobe's blood flow and activity.

1. **Cerebellum:** coordination, graceful athleticism, precision in movement, balance

2. **Occipital Lobe:** makes sense of visual information so that we are able to understand it, architectural skills, and spatial orientation (like a 3-D map) of objects in the visual field

3. **Temporal Lobe:** memory, auditory processing, vocabulary, and musical ability

4. **Parietal lobe:** sensation, speech, language comprehension, attention, and calculations

5. **Frontal lobe:** reasoning, planning, movement, creative problem solving, higher forms of math and creative speech, spirituality, the will, and where emotional intelligence and general intelligence come together

Depressed

Recovered

Notice the greatest improvement of activity is in the frontal lobe.

WHAT THE FRONTAL LOBE DESIRES

Carbohydrates are used almost exclusively by the brain for optimal function.

Peak brain function requires an adequate supply of:

- » Omega-3
- » Folate B_6
- » B_{12}
- » Vitamin D
- » Vitamin C
- » Antioxidants

VITAMIN D

- » Magnesium and vitamin B_6 also needed to convert to brain tryptophan to serotonin
- » Calcium and vitamin D needed to convert serotonin into melatonin

THE POWER OF WHOLE PLANT FOODS

- » Exceeds that of their component parts
- » One cup of cooked kale has 50mg of vitamin C and 13 IU of vitamin E
- » The antioxidant potential of one cup of kale is equal to 800mg of vitamin C and 1100 units of vitamin E

THE ANTIOXIDANT TOP TEN FRUITS

10. Tomato
9. Apple
8. Banana
7. White grapes
6. Grapefruit, pink

5. Kiwifruit
4. _____ ✎ 8-b
3. Orange
2. Plum
1. Strawberry

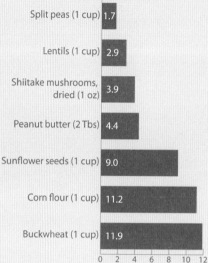

Foods High in Niacin (B_3)

Food	Value
Split peas (1 cup)	1.7
Lentils (1 cup)	2.9
Shiitake mushrooms, dried (1 oz)	3.9
Peanut butter (2 Tbs)	4.4
Sunflower seeds (1 cup)	9.0
Corn flour (1 cup)	11.2
Buckwheat (1 cup)	11.9

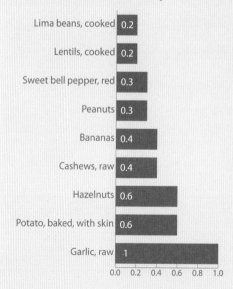

Foods High in Vitamin B_6 (mg/100g)

Food	Value
Lima beans, cooked	0.2
Lentils, cooked	0.2
Sweet bell pepper, red	0.3
Peanuts	0.3
Bananas	0.4
Cashews, raw	0.4
Hazelnuts	0.6
Potato, baked, with skin	0.6
Garlic, raw	1

THE ANTIOXIDANT TOP TEN VEGETABLES

10. Corn
9. Onion
8. Red bell pepper
7. Beets
6. Broccoli

5. Alfalfa sprouts
4. Brussels sprouts
3. Spinach
2. Kale
1. _____ 🔍 8-c

VITAMIN D[1]

» Those with higher blood vitamin D levels perform better in paying attention in tests measuring processing speed of the brain

» Improves mood in those with low vitamin D levels

» Improves winter depression

CALCIUM IN COMMON FOODS

FOOD ITEM	AMOUNT	CALC (mg)
Oatmeal	1c.	19
Lentils	1c.	38
Quinoa grain	1c.	102
Rutabagas	1c.	115
Dandelion greens	1c.	147
Mustard greens	1c.	152
Baked beans	1c.	154
Sesame seeds	2 Tbs.	176
Blackstrap cane molasses	1 Tbs.	176
Kale	1c.	179
Turnip greens	1c.	249
Filberts/Hazelnuts (dried)	1c.	254
Green soybeans	1c.	261
Figs (dried)	1c.	269
Whole milk	1c.	290
Amaranth grain	1c.	298
Nonfat skim milk	1c.	301
Collard greens	1c.	357
Carob flour	1c.	358
Lambsquarters	1c.	464

Foods High in Zinc (mg)

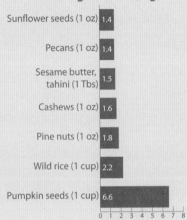

	mg
Sunflower seeds (1 oz)	1.4
Pecans (1 oz)	1.4
Sesame butter, tahini (1 Tbs)	1.5
Cashews (1 oz)	1.6
Pine nuts (1 oz)	1.8
Wild rice (1 cup)	2.2
Pumpkin seeds (1 cup)	6.6

Foods Rich in Vitamin C (mg/100g)

FOOD ITEM	VITAMIN C (mg)
Acerola cherry	1677
Guavas, common	228
Sweet red bell peppers, raw	128
Kale, raw	120
Broccoli, raw	89
Cauliflower, raw	89
Brussels sprouts, raw	85
Kiwifruit, raw	75
Oranges, raw	71
Strawberries, raw	59

Foods High in Magnesium

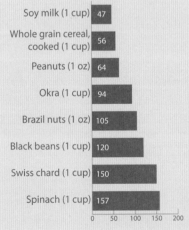

Soy milk (1 cup)	47
Whole grain cereal, cooked (1 cup)	56
Peanuts (1 oz)	64
Okra (1 cup)	94
Brazil nuts (1 oz)	105
Black beans (1 cup)	120
Swiss chard (1 cup)	150
Spinach (1 cup)	157

ENHANCING FRONTAL LOBE FUNCTION, part 2

MUSIC

Melodious beautiful music where the melody and harmony are more prominent than the rhythm.

DEFINITE FRONTAL LOBE HITS

» Alcohol, nicotine, illicit drugs

» Benzodiazipines

» Low carbohydrate diet

» Entertainment television/gaming

» MTV viewer

» Other addictions

» Frequent sexual arousal _____ ✎ 8-d
  of marriage

» No regular scriptural study or abstract thinking

» Habitually going against your conscience`

TAKE CARE OF YOUR FRONTAL LOBE

» Protect it from mechanical injury

» Supply it with good oxygen

» Give it good nutrition

» Get adequate sunshine

» Exercise it

» Control the inputs

» Prevent or control disease that affects it

STRONG RELIGIOUS FAITH HELPS SPEED RECOVERY FROM DEPRESSION[2]

» "Depressed patients with higher intrinsic religiosity scores had more rapid remissions than patients with lower scores."

» Patients recovered from depression 70% sooner with every 10 point increase in the religiosity assessment score. External religious activity had much less of an impact.

AS A MEANS OF INTELLECTUAL TRAINING

» The Bible is effective. The greatness of its themes, the dignified simplicity of its utterances, the beauty of its imagery, quicken and uplift the thoughts.

» "No other study can impart such mental power as does the effort to grasp the truths of revelation."

—EDUCATION 124

RECOMMEND A STUDY OF THE BOOK OF DANIEL

» Each chapter begins with a disappointment and transitions into an appointment!

» Applying the principles of each chapter reveals keys for long lasting success

» The last six chapters deals with symbols, prophecy, and high abstract thought

» This will improve frontal lobe function

TREATMENTS FOR DEPRESSION

» Attempt to find the _____ ✎ 8-e

» Enhance frontal lobe function

» Avoid frontal lobe suppressants

» Get adequate sleep

» Get aerobic physical exercise

» Utilize hydrotherapy

These were more noble than those in Thessalonica, in that they received the word with all readiness of mind, and searched the scriptures daily, whether those things were so.

—Doctor Luke from ACTS 17:11

» Breathing exercises

» Classical music therapy

» Avoid negative thinking

» Increase reading and contemplating good spiritual material

» Increase your faith and devotion to God

» Choose relationships that can enhance and support this plan

RESEARCH[3]

» Taking part in group action to help bring about positive change can be good for your physical and mental health

» "The take-home message from this research therefore might be that people should get more involved in campaigns, struggles, and leading positive group programs, not only in the wider interest of the common good, but also for their own personal good."

» The results emerged from in-depth interviews with nearly 40 people from a variety of backgrounds

» Between them, they had more than 160 experiences of group action to bring about positive changes

» Such was the strength of the feelings they experienced that the effects appear to be sustained over a period of time

» "Empowering events were almost without exception described as _____ ✎ 8-f occasions."

» "Participants experienced a deep sense of happiness and even euphoria in being involved in teaming with others for positive change. Simply recounting the events in the interview brought a smile to the face of the interviewees."

» For wisdom is better than rubies; and all the things that may be desired are not to be compared to it.

—PROVERBS 8:11

The follow up Daniel study will help you find the keys in each chapter that make the transition from disappointment to appointments possible. The understanding and application of every key is critically important to long term success.

_____
_____
_____
_____
_____
_____
_____
_____
_____
_____
_____
_____

⚙ What You Learned

» Methods to increase blood flow and frontal lobe activity

» Attentive listening to classical music aids in circulation of the frontal lobe

» Scripture and religious faith positively impacts mental health and the intellect

Reading Prescription

» *Depression: the Way Out,* chapter 9, and review chapter 10

» Chapter in the book of Proverbs that corresponds with each day's date

LIFESTYLE IN ACTION

The most important organ in the body is your brain. This is both your planning and command center. Achieving your dreams does not require luck. It requires you to think, plan, reason, manage your emotions, solve problems, and make wise decisions—all an accomplishment of a well-functioning frontal lobe. Positive lifestyle behaviors and thoughts, over time, can enhance the circulation and activity of the frontal lobe. From purchasing a car, land, or a home, to what investment to make, what advice to take, who you choose to pursue as close friends, and what job to take, a healthy frontal lobe is required to produce wins in all of these areas. Consider adopting the list below as part of your strategic plan for both short and long term success. You will reap the bountiful rewards both professionally and personally.

» Eat a high anti-oxidant, plant-based diet rich in omega-3, tryptophan, and natural carbohydrates

» Improve serotonin levels; incorporate light therapy; get adequate amounts of vitamin D

» Practice daily gratitude exercises

» Engage in physical exercise; gardening; work with your hands in 3 dimensions

» Listen to uplifting, melodious music; learn a new skill or instrument

» Remove entertainment television, video games, and syncopated or heavy rhythm music

» Commit to live a truth filled moral lifestyle that is helpful and compassionate to others

» Read Scripture or spiritual material out loud, if possible; interpret or create proverbs

» Write down and carry through creative thoughts that are useful to yourself or others

Food

Nutrition is important to keep your frontal lobe functioning well. Try a new, healthy dish with unique flavors that you are not accustomed too. Many recipes taste just as good with less sugar. Take all this newfound knowledge concerning sugar, whole plant foods, the top 10 antioxidant fruits, the top 10 antioxidant vegetables and incorporate it in your own recipes. If you need ideas look back through the food charts. (Example: I will commit to no sugar for one month. I will add 2-3 antioxidant fruits and vegetables to my diet each week.)

Music

Few people understand the powerful influence that music has on the frontal lobe. Music enters the brain through its emotional regions. Depending on the type of music, it can either influence the brain beneficially or detrimentally. It surrounds you as you ride in elevators, shop in the mall, drive in your car, and watch television. Music has become such a common part of your daily life that sometimes you do not even notice its presence. What if music affects your problem solving and decision-making skills?

What if listening to certain types of music causes you to perform poorly on cognitive tasks and become stressed? Music therapists describe that certain types of music, such as rock with its syncopated rhythm, bypass the frontal lobe and thus escape your ability to reason and make informed judgments. Evidence suggests that rock music, like entertainment television, can produce a hypnotic effect. Since you know that music affects your brain, you will want to listen to the right kind of music, knowing that your abilities will improve while driving in a car, performing surgery in an operating room, or any another tasks.[4]

Action Step 8.1	Activities to Enhance the Frontal Lobe

There are more styles of classical music then there are genres of all other types of music combined. What projects can you work on this week while listening to classical music that enhances or goes along with the project? For instance, a lullaby when you are getting ready for bed and reading pleasant material such as a Psalm or a Proverb, or a Hungarian dance while you are dusting the house.

Project/Activity	Composer/Musical Selection
1.	
2.	
3.	

Listening to classical music:

1. Increases interest in reading and learning
2. Strengthens brainpower
3. Encourages good lifestyle habits
4. Allows frontal lobe to filter information
5. Encourages fitness
6. Increases productivity
7. Strengthens creativity
8. Decreases irritability
9. Increases spiritual pursuits
10. Improves self-control

The impact of music on shaping the character (and hence the frontal lobe) was recognized at least 23 centuries ago. Aristotle, the Greek philosopher wrote, "...when one listens to music that imitates a certain passion he becomes imbued with the same passion. If over a long time he habitually listens to the kind of music that rouses ignoble [degraded or vulgar] passions, his whole character will be shaped to an ignoble form. In short, if one listens to the wrong kind of music he will become the wrong kind of person; conversely, if he listens to the right kind of music he will tend to become the right kind of person."[5]

The Science of Prayer

Prayer is a balanced form of meditation that, unlike most types of meditation, actually involves and strengthens the frontal lobe. The purpose of prayer is not so much to move God, but to let God move you in the right direction. Often this is best accomplished by going to a place where no one else can hear you, then reading out loud scriptural or spiritual material, such as the chapters entitled "Mind Cure," "Help in Daily Living," "In Contact with Others," "Development and Service" from the classical best-seller book *Ministry of Healing*. Whenever you read a promise, mark it in the Bible or the book in a certain color, and while talking to God claim that promise for you. Whenever you read a command, mark it in a different color and then ask God if you are in compliance with it. If you sense you are not, analyze how you can change your thoughts or behavior to get in compliance with it. Tell God what you are planning to change and ask Him for help to follow through. Praying out loud can help retain your focus and decrease the likelihood of being distracted during this important exercise. This can powerfully enhance the frontal lobe while being thought provoking, life-changing (in a positive way), and enjoyable at the same time.

Action Step 8.2   Review

Evaluate yourself with the chart below using the following scale, circling the appropriate letter (A, B, or C). The number in parenthesis indicates the session where each Lifestyle in Action is found.

A. *I have habitually changed/added/been consistent with these activities.*

B. *I have half-heartedly changed or added these activities to my schedule.*

C. *I have yet to change or add these activities to my weekly routine.*

	A	B	C
1. No critical or negative speech (1)	○	○	○
2. Adequate water intake (1)	○	○	○
3. Exercise and interval training (1, 2)	○	○	○
4. Classical music therapy (1)	○	○	○
5. Deep breathing exercises (2)	○	○	○
6. Light therapy; good light exposure (2)	○	○	○
7. Massage (2)	○	○	○
8. Contrast showers (2)	○	○	○
9. Tryptophan intake (3)	○	○	○
10. Vitamin B_{12} intake (3)	○	○	○
11. Omega-3 intake (3)	○	○	○
12. Folic acid intake (3)	○	○	○
13. Cholesterol intake reduced/eliminated (3)	○	○	○
14. Plant-based diet (3)	○	○	○
15. Analyze your thoughts for distortions (4)	○	○	○
16. Reconstructing your thoughts (4)	○	○	○
17. Working with your hands (1)	○	○	○

Are you applying these concepts in your life? If yes, congratulations! If you are still incorporating these in your life, talk with your support person to hold you accountable and KEEP GOING!

Twenty Week Program

Take the Nedley Depression and Anxiety Assessment Test (DAAT). Remember that this is a 20 week program and you have only completed 8 weeks (if you have done one session per week until now). If you find out that you still have hits beyond just the genetic and developmental, you likely still have significant work to do. See what you can change in your life to get your hits down to three or less, preferably two or less.

The results are in. This program works ONLY if you work the program. It CONTINUES to work only if you continue to work the program. Review this workbook throughout the twenty weeks; continue to make positive lifestyle changes and the sky is the limit to your happiness and life satisfaction. Then get someone else in need connected with this program. The world will then become a better place, one person at a time.

If you do not achieve the results you were hoping for, call the nurse case manager of the residential *Nedley Depression and Anxiety Recovery Program*™ and go to a place where you WILL get the professional help needed to turn your life around. That number is 888-778-4445. Don't delay. Depression and/or anxiety does not have to be a lifelong condition with all its resultant complications. You CAN live a life free from depression and anxiety, full of satisfaction and success.

Action Step 8.3	**Follow-up**

Write the dates for the follow-up Nedley Depression and Anxiety Recover Alumni meetings and any additional programs you are interested in attending.

1. Program: _____ Date: _____

2. Program: _____ Date: _____

3. Program: _____ Date: _____

4. Program: _____ Date: _____

BE THE NEXT SUCCESS STORY

I have a great business and have made a lot of money. However, my arrogance, alcoholism, and womanizing caught up with me and I began a downward spiral. I became persistently very uncertain about things. I was not feeling well and was anxious all the time. Since I got a hold of the *Nedley Depression and Anxiety Recovery Program*™ material, I have been implementing all that I learn. There are a lot of new things I would like to incorporate into my life, but the wonderful benefits I have experienced cannot be compared to anything else and are worth all the effort. I have not only recovered from my alcoholism, but am also nicotine free—a bonus I was not expecting. I now have what it takes to rebuild my marriage. With all of the tools that the program taught and offered me, I am much more confident in my future plans. Now I wake up ready to face the day! What a difference! I AM BACK!

—M. K., Canada

When I started the program I realized that there was a lot of nutritional information that would benefit me, and it did! I had a hard time sleeping. I'd wake up in the middle of the night and couldn't get back to sleep. Now, even if I wake up in the middle of the night, I am able to go right back to sleep. I especially recommend this program to anyone who has difficulty with sleep, stress, or getting along with other people.

—A. V., California

This program is very useful, especially for parents and teenagers. Your quality of life depends on your physical, mental, and spiritual health. This program reveals how your habits of life affect these three areas and ultimately helps you to deal with anxiety and depression. The program is an outstanding self-help program for those who are suffering from high levels of stress, anxiety, and depression. It's the best thing I've been associated with since I have been in the military. While the military has a great recovery program for those who experience alcohol and drug addictions, this one by far exceeds their programs. Besides helping with drug, alcohol, and smoking addictions, this program can also help recover from many other addictions including soft drinks and chocolate. I am now back to work and earning even a better income than I had before I experienced depression.

—N. L., Georgia

I really like this program since it gets to the root of the problem rather than just treating symptoms. At night, I couldn't shut my mind off. I had been a smoker for 30 years. As a result of this comprehensive program, I was able to get the help I needed to quit. I am now able to sleep without feelings of anxiety. I would recommend the program first to anyone who has depression or anxiety, and then to anyone who is close to someone who suffers from depression or anxiety.

—J. S., New York

Following this program for just 8-weeks has not only eradicated my depression and anxiety but has also helped me spiritually, mentally, and physically.

—P. D., Australia

HEALTHY LIFESTYLE SCORECARD

DAILY ACTIVITIES	SUNDAY	MONDAY	TUESDAY	WEDNESDAY	THURSDAY	FRIDAY	SATURDAY
AVOID NEGATIVE SPEECH							
CLASSICAL MUSIC							
WATER							
EXERCISE							
SLEEP							
DEEP BREATHING							
LIGHT THERAPY							
PROVERBS							
OMEGA-3							
GRATITUDE JOURNAL							

The Healthy Lifestyle Scorecard includes ten categories that are important to your recovery. For each category make a daily entry.

HEALTHY LIFESTYLE SCORECARD

DAILY ACTIVITIES	SUNDAY	MONDAY	TUESDAY	WEDNESDAY	THURSDAY	FRIDAY	SATURDAY
AVOID NEGATIVE SPEECH							
CLASSICAL MUSIC							
WATER							
EXERCISE							
SLEEP							
DEEP BREATHING							
LIGHT THERAPY							
PROVERBS							
OMEGA-3							
GRATITUDE JOURNAL							

The Healthy Lifestyle Scorecard includes ten categories that are important to your recovery. For each category make a daily entry.

HEALTHY LIFESTYLE SCORECARD

DAILY ACTIVITIES	SUNDAY	MONDAY	TUESDAY	WEDNESDAY	THURSDAY	FRIDAY	SATURDAY
AVOID NEGATIVE SPEECH							
CLASSICAL MUSIC							
WATER							
EXERCISE							
SLEEP							
DEEP BREATHING							
LIGHT THERAPY							
PROVERBS							
OMEGA-3							
GRATITUDE JOURNAL							

The Healthy Lifestyle Scorecard includes ten categories that are important to your recovery. For each category make a daily entry.

HEALTHY LIFESTYLE SCORECARD

Session 4

DAILY ACTIVITIES	SUNDAY	MONDAY	TUESDAY	WEDNESDAY	THURSDAY	FRIDAY	SATURDAY
AVOID NEGATIVE SPEECH							
CLASSICAL MUSIC							
WATER							
EXERCISE							
SLEEP							
DEEP BREATHING							
LIGHT THERAPY							
PROVERBS							
OMEGA-3							
GRATITUDE JOURNAL							

The Healthy Lifestyle Scorecard includes ten categories that are important to your recovery. For each category make a daily entry.

HEALTHY LIFESTYLE SCORECARD

Session 5

DAILY ACTIVITIES	SUNDAY	MONDAY	TUESDAY	WEDNESDAY	THURSDAY	FRIDAY	SATURDAY
AVOID NEGATIVE SPEECH							
CLASSICAL MUSIC							
WATER							
EXERCISE							
SLEEP							
DEEP BREATHING							
LIGHT THERAPY							
PROVERBS							
OMEGA-3							
GRATITUDE JOURNAL							

The Healthy Lifestyle Scorecard includes ten categories that are important to your recovery. For each category make a daily entry.

HEALTHY LIFESTYLE SCORECARD

DAILY ACTIVITIES	SUNDAY	MONDAY	TUESDAY	WEDNESDAY	THURSDAY	FRIDAY	SATURDAY
AVOID NEGATIVE SPEECH							
CLASSICAL MUSIC							
WATER							
EXERCISE							
SLEEP							
DEEP BREATHING							
LIGHT THERAPY							
PROVERBS							
OMEGA-3							
GRATITUDE JOURNAL							

The Healthy Lifestyle Scorecard includes ten categories that are important to your recovery. For each category make a daily entry.

HEALTHY LIFESTYLE SCORECARD

DAILY ACTIVITIES	SUNDAY	MONDAY	TUESDAY	WEDNESDAY	THURSDAY	FRIDAY	SATURDAY
AVOID NEGATIVE SPEECH							
CLASSICAL MUSIC							
WATER							
EXERCISE							
SLEEP							
DEEP BREATHING							
LIGHT THERAPY							
PROVERBS							
OMEGA-3							
GRATITUDE JOURNAL							

The Healthy Lifestyle Scorecard includes ten categories that are important to your recovery. For each category make a daily entry.

HEALTHY LIFESTYLE SCORECARD

DAILY ACTIVITIES	SUNDAY	MONDAY	TUESDAY	WEDNESDAY	THURSDAY	FRIDAY	SATURDAY
AVOID NEGATIVE SPEECH							
CLASSICAL MUSIC							
WATER							
EXERCISE							
SLEEP							
DEEP BREATHING							
LIGHT THERAPY							
PROVERBS							
OMEGA-3							
GRATITUDE JOURNAL							

The Healthy Lifestyle Scorecard includes ten categories that are important to your recovery. For each category make a daily entry.

ANSWER KEY

SESSION 1

1-a	cells
1-b	mental
1-c	increased
1-d	women
1-e	men
1-f	disability
1-g	fatigue
1-h	seven times
1-i	personal
1-j	headache
1-k	anger
1-l	murder
1-m	ongoing war
1-n	practical
1-o	ten
1-p	Frontal Lobe
1-q	Spirituality
1-r	blood flow
1-s	empathy
1-t	memory
1-u	reduced
1-v	discernment
1-w	family
1-x	emotional
1-y	Melodious

SESSION 2

2-a	controlling
2-b	acute
2-c	impair
2-d	Moderate
2-e	Regular
2-f	far less
2-g	exercise
2-h	Athlete
2-i	serotonin
2-j	negative
2-k	15
2-l	temporary
2-m	regular
2-n	libido

SESSION 3

3-a	nutrition
3-b	high
3-c	low
3-d	cholesterol
3-e	middle-age
3-f	mercury
3-g	breakfast

SESSION 4

4-a	cognitive
4-b	goals
4-c	feelings
4-d	values
4-e	beliefs
4-f	feelings
4-g	myself
4-h	positive
4-i	chance
4-j	changing
4-k	disqualified

SESSION 5

5-a	desire
5-b	happy
5-c	addiction
5-d	thoughts
5-e	technology
5-f	healthy
5-g	rely
5-h	patience

SESSION 6

6-a	resistance
6-b	self Inflicted
6-c	oversensitive
6-d	acknowledge
6-e	merciful stance
6-f	Irrational
6-g	prefer

SESSION 7

7-a	grief
7-b	eight
7-c	3 to 12
7-d	tragic
7-e	tasks
7-f	life-changing
7-g	meaningful

SESSION 8

8-a	medical condition
8-b	red grapes
8-c	garlic
8-d	outside
8-e	cause
8-f	joyous

LYRICS TO DEPRESSION AND ANXIETY RECOVERY HYMNS

Onward Christian Soldiers*

Onward, Christian soldiers!
Marching as to war,
Fighting false perceptions,
Feelings, pride, and more.
Christ has given battle tools:
Reason, conscience, TRUTH!
Forward into battle,
Use our WILLS to choose!

Onward, Christian soldiers!
Marching as to war,
With the cross of Jesus
Going on before.

When the Spirit of truth is come,
To all truth He guides.
There is comfort, peace with truth;
There is none with lies.
By deception, Satan gains
Power o'er the mind.
Through the Word of Truth, the
Spirit subdues humankind.

Onward, Christian soldiers!
Marching as to war,
With the words of Jesus
Going on before.

Minds are much like gardens;
Seeds of truth can sprout.
We must tend them constantly;
Weeds can choke them out.
Gardening is no easy task!
We must do our part.
Christians must be vigilant-
Life's a battle march!

Onward, Christian soldiers-
Women men and youth,
Every thought we must yield
To the Spirit of truth.

I Surrender All*

All to Jesus I surrender,
every thought I bring to You,
casting down imaginations,
captive only to what's true.

I surrender all!
I surrender all!
You desire Truth within me;
I surrender all.

All to Jesus I surrender
What I think will certainly shape
perceptions of experience,
and become a part of me.

I surrender all!
I surrender all!
You desire Truth within me;
I surrender all.

True and honest, just and pure,
and lovely things of good report,
if there's virtue, if there's praise,
my thoughts will only be these
sort.

I surrender all!
I surrender all!
You desire Truth within me;
I surrender all.

I'm drawn by my fallen feelings
to regret, so I must test.
Use my will, and reason,
conscience;
am I worshipping the Best?

I surrender all!
I surrender all!
What I live for is my Master,
I surrender all.

When I fear that I'm worth
nothing,
there's a Truth that sets me free:
I am valued by the price paid,
GOD HIMSELF has died for me!

I surrender all;
intimate to You,
"knowing" Truth is more than
knowledge,
I surrender all.

REFERENCES

SESSION 1

1. Kessler RC, Chiu WT, Demler O, Walters EE. Prevalence, severity, and comorbidity of twelve-month DSM-IV disorders in the National Comorbidity Survey Replication (NCS-R). Archives of General Psychiatry, 2005 Jun;62(6):617-27.

2. Klerman G, Weissman M. Increasing Rates of Depression. JAMA. 1989;261(15):2229-2235.

3. Weissman M, Wickramaratne P, et al. The Changing Rate of Major Depression: Cross-National Comparisons. JAMA. 1992;268(21):3098-3105.

4. Birmaher B, Ryan ND, Williamson DE, et al. Childhood and adolescent depression: a review of the past 10 years. Part I. J Am Acad Child Adolesc Psychiatry. 1996;35(11):1427-39.

5. Greenberg, P, Fournier A, et al. The Economic Burden of Adults With Major Depressive Disorder in the United States (2005 and 2010). J Clin Psychiatry. 2015;76(2):155-62.

6. Stewart WF, Ricci JA, Chee E, Hahn SR, Morganstein D. Cost of lost productive work time among US workers with depression. JAMA. 2003;289(23):31.

7. Smith, J. P., & Smith, G. C. Long-term economic costs of psychological problems during childhood. Social Science & Medicine, 2010;71:110-115.71, 110-115.

8. Lipchok GL, Rains JC, et al. Recurrent headache: a neglected women's health problem. Women's Health Issues 1998 Jan-Feb;8(1):60-64.

9. Michelson D, Sratakis C, et al. Bone mineral density in women with depression. NEJM 1996 Oct 17;335(16):1176

10. Jonas BS, Lando DK, et al. Symptoms of Anxiety and Depression as Risk Factors for Development of Asthma. J Appl Biobehav Research 1999;4-91-110.

11. Berndt ER, Koran LM, et al. Lost human capital from early-onset chronic depression. Am J Psychiatry. 2000 Jun;157(6):940-947.

12. Penninx, Brenda WJH, et al. "Depressive symptoms and physical decline in community-dwelling older persons." JAMA 279.21 (1998): 1720-1726.

13. Everson SA, et al. Depressive symptoms and increased risk of stroke mortality over a 29 year period. Arch Intern Med 1998 May 25;158(10):1133-1138.

14. Hippisley-Cox, J. Depression as a risk factor for ischemic heart disease in men: population-based case-control study. BMJ 1998;316:1714-1719.

15. Takeida K, Nishi M, Miyake H. Mental depression and death in elderly persons. J Epidemiol 1997 Dec;7(4):210-213.

16. Angst J, Angst F, Stassen HH. Suicide risk in patients with major depressive disorder. J Clinical Psychiatry 1990;60 Suppl 2:57-62;discussion 75-76,113-116.

17. Potter, LB. Suicide in youth; a public health framework. J Am Acad Child Adolesc Psychiatry 1998 May;341:1583

18. U.S. Department of Health and Human Services: Mental Health: A Report of the Surgeon General. U.S. Department of Health and Human Services, Substance Abuse and Mental Health Service Administration, Center for Mental Health Services, National Institutes of Health, National Institute of Mental Health, Rockville, Maryland, 1999 p 245.

19. Baker LB, Conroy DE, Kenney WL. Dehydration impairs vigilance-related attention in male basketball players. Med Sci Sports Exerc 2007;39: 976–983.

20. Gopinathan PM, Pichan G, Sharma VM. Role of dehydration in heat stress-induced variations in mental performance. Arch Environ Health 1988; 43: 15–17.

21. Cian C, Barraud PA, Melin B, Raphel C. Effects of fluid ingestion on cognitive function after heat stress or exercise-induced dehydration. Int J Psychophysiol 2001;42: 243–251.

22. Kempton KJ, et al. Dehydration affects brain structure and function in healthy adolescents. Human Brain Mapping 2011;71-79.

23. McKinney CH, Antoni MH, et al. Effects of guided imagery and music (GIM) therapy on mood and cortisol in health adults. Health Psychology 1997;16;390-400.

SESSION 2

1. Hyman S. Mental health: depression needs large human-genetics studies. Nature. 2014;515(7526):189-91.

2. Depressive and bipolar mood disorders. Scientific American Medicine 2000 May:9.

3. Nedley, Neil. Depression: the Way Out. Ardmore, OK. Nedley Publishing;2005.

4. Strawbridge WJ, Deleger S, Roberts RE, Kaplan GA. Physical activity reduces the risk of subsequent depression for older adults. Am J Epidemiol. 2002;156(4):328-34.

5. Andreas Ströhle. Physical activity, exercise, depression and anxiety disorders. J Neural Transm 2009;116:777–784.

6. Blumenthal JA, Babyak MA, Doraiswamy PM, et al. Exercise and pharmacotherapy in the treatment of major depressive disorder. Psychosom Med. 2007;69(7):587-96.

7. Herring MP, O'connor PJ, Dishman RK. The effect of exercise training on anxiety symptoms among patients: a systematic review. Arch Intern Med. 2010;170(4):321-31.

8. Broocks A, Bandelow B, Pekrun G, et al. Comparison of aerobic exercise, clomipramine, and placebo in treatment of panic disorder. Am J Psychiatry 1998;155 (5) 603- 609.

9. Shirani A, St. Louis E. Illuminating Rationale and Uses for Light Therapy. J Clin Sleep Med. 2009 April 15; 5(2): 155–163.

10. Lam R, Levitt A, Levitan R, et al. The Can-SAD Study: A Randomized Controlled Trial of the Effectiveness of Light Therapy and Fluoxetine in Patients With Winter Seasonal Affective Disorder. American Journal of Psychiatry. 2006;163(5):805-812.

11. Maas J, Verheij R, et al. Morbidity is related to a green living environment. J Epidemiol Community Health 2009;63:967-973.

12. Suglia S, Wright R, et al. Association between lung function and cognition among children in a prospective birth cohort study. Psychosom Med. 2008 Apr; 70(3): 356–362.

13. Yoon I, Kripke D, et al. Luteinizing hormone following light exposure in healthy young men. Neuroscience Letters 2003;341:25-28.

14. Robinson-Whelen S. Journal of Personality and Social Psychology. 1997;73:1345-1353.

15. Lieverse R, Van someren EJ, et al. Bright light treatment in